SCHOLASTIC COLLECTIONS

Compiled by Peter Morrell

Songs

© 1992 Scholastic Publications Ltd

Published by Scholastic Publications Ltd,
Villiers House,
Clarendon Avenue,
Leamington Spa,
Warwickshire CV32 5PR

Compiler Peter Morrell
Editor Gina Burnes
Sub-editors Jane Wright and Barry Krüger
Series designer Joy White
Designer David Harrop
Illustrations & cover illustration Lynn Breeze

Designed using Aldus Pagemaker
Processed by Salvo Print and Design, Leamington Spa
Artwork by David Harban Design, Warwick
Printed in Great Britain by Ebenezer Baylis & Son Ltd,
Worcester

British Library Cataloguing-in-Publication Data
A catalogue record for this book is
available from the British Library.

ISBN 0-590-53022-4

Contents

A YEAR FULL OF SONGS

ME AND MY WORLD

THE WORLD WE LIVE IN

EARTH, AIR, FIRE AND WATER

HOW DID WE TRAVEL?

LOOKING BACK, LOOKING FORWARD

A YEAR FULL OF SONGS

Peter Morrell

1. We'll sing a song ev-'ry day of the year. We'll sing out loud and we'll Sing out clear. So join with us ev-'ry-one come a-long and we'll *(clap)* sing a year full of ___ songs.

2. The seasons change as the year unfolds
From summer warmth to the winter cold.
So join with us, ev'ryone come along
And we'll *(clap)* sing a year full of songs.

3. There's birthdays, feast days and
   holidays too,
These special times just for me and you.
So join with us, ev'ryone come along
And we'll *(clap)* sing a year full of songs.

4. The year is full of excitement and fun,
Those play-time days in the summer sun.
So join with us, ev'ryone come along
And we'll *(clap)* sing a year full of songs.

Round the seasons

Ian Henderson Begg

1. Win - ter is the sea - son when All the trees are bare:

Frost and snow and bit - ter winds — Pen - e - trate the air.

2. Springtime is the season when
Leaves begin to show:
Warming sun and gentle rain
Make the flowers grow.

3. Summer is the season when
Plants and trees grow strong:
Sun is high, it's warm and fine,
Night's short, day is long.

4. Autumn's when the leaves do fall,
Harvest's gathered in:
Days are getting shorter as the
Year comes to its end.

(This song can be sung as a round.)

Pancake song

Music by Peter Morrell and words by Elizabeth Chapman

Square dance

(Spoken) It's Shrove Tues-day don't you know, Time for pan-cakes let's go!

(Sung) Whisked the eggs and weighed the flour___ Put them in the mix-ing bowl.

Add-ed milk and then some wa-ter, How it thrilled me to the soul!

Stirred the mix-ture, melt-ted but-ter, Oh I took the great-test care,

You'd be en-vious if you'd seen me. Real-ly wish that you'd been there

___ ere ___ ere. Scrape the pan-cake off the ceil-ing,

Wash the bat-ter from the floor, I tell you that I will nev-er

make these pan-cakes any, any, any, any more___ no more!

2.(Spoken) Mix the batter in the bowl,
It's quite good for – the soul!
(Sung) Things were sizzling, pancakes cooking,
It was really going well,
Then I had this inspiration
If you listen I will tell.
Grasped the handle, flexed my muscles,
Got all ready for the toss.
Oh my friends, a tragic story,
My heart's breaking at the loss.

Chorus

3.(Spoken) Take your fryin' pan by the hand,
Toss the pancake – watch it land.
(Sung) Flipped the handle, watched the pancake,
As it floated thro' the air.
When I held the pan to catch it
My poor pancake wasn't there.
Saw it splatter on the vinyl,
Watched it scatter on the floor,
Made a promise, and I'll keep it,
Won't make pancakes any more.

Chorus

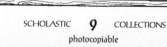

A king, riding on a donkey

David Moses

Chorus

2.*(Voice 1)* The shout we raise is a shout of praise as the king rides by.
Yet who would guess in a week, or less, that the king would die?
(Voice 2 as verse 1.)

Chorus

3.*(Voice 1)* We cover the street beneath his feet, as He rides in power.
But then, in shame, we deny His name in His dying hour.
(Voice 2 as verse 1.)

Chorus

4.*(Voice 1)* He weeps to hear how we shout and cheer, for He clearly sees
That for all our glee, we fail to see His gift of peace.
(Voice 2 as verse 1.)

Chorus

5.*(Voice 1)* So, as we stand and sing 'Hosanna, Mighty Lord',
Don't sing so loud that you can't hear His Holy Word.
(Voice 2 as verse 1.)

Chorus

Entering Jerusalem

Lesley Funge

1. Cut a branch, cut a branch from the palm tree, Lay it on the stree — — — t, Sweep the dust, sweep the dust from a-round the lit-tle don-key's feet. En-ter-ing Je-ru-sa-lem, wave your branch of palm, Keep our Lord and mas-ter free from harm.

Chorus

Shout Ho-san-na Je-sus is the King. King of

2. Spread your cloak, spread your cloak, make a carpet,
Spread it on the road.
Little colt, little colt, you do carry such a precious load,
Following the prophecy, a cloak upon your back,
Trotting gently on the royal track.

Chorus

3. He is here, He is here, King of Israel,
Praise to God on high,
'He will save us from the Romans,' hear the people cry.
Welcome to Jerusalem, Hosanna, shout hooray.
Teach us how to kneel and pray, to hear and do all that you say,
Teach us, Lord, to follow you day by day.

Once upon a summer's day

Ann Bryant

Steady, bouncy

1. Once u - pon a sum-mer's day the car - ni - val danced,— Oh there was

fun in the streets__ when__ the an - i - mals pranced,__ And

I danced a - long with the crowd __ HEY! HEY! Yes

I danced a-long with the crowd!   crowd.

8ve

2. Once upon a summer's day the carnival sang,
Oh there was fun in the streets when the rockets went BANG!
And I sang along with the crowd HEY! HEY!
Yes I sang along with the crowd!

3. Once upon a summer's day the carnival cheered,
Oh there was fun in the streets when the juggler appeared,
And I cheered along with the crowd HOORAY!
Yes I cheered along with the crowd!

4. Once upon a summer's day the carnival clapped,
Oh there was fun in the streets when the tap dancers tapped,
And I clapped along with the crowd (CLAP, CLAP).
Yes I clapped along with the crowd (CLAP, CLAP).

Going back to school

David Moses

Go - ing back to school, go - ing back to school, Ho - li-days are

great, but I can't wait to be go - ing back to school.

1. All___ the chil - dren in the play - ground, Laugh - ing, talk - ing,

Rac - ing, walk - ing, Jump -ing up and down. Act -ing like a clown.

Chorus

2. All the children in assembly,
Singing, playing,
Listening, praying.
Stories in a book,
Things to make you look.

Chorus

3. All the children in the classroom,
Writing, drawing,
Mixing, pouring
Water in a tray,
Making things with clay.

Chorus

4. All the children on their first day,
New things, new place,
New friend, new face,
Being on your own
Until it's time for home.

Chorus

5. Children on the apparatus,
Jump high, crouch low,
Walk on tiptoe,
Running round the hall,
Stretching very tall.

Wake up, wake up, wake up

Debbie Campbell

Wake up, _ wake up, wake up. _ Get out of bed _ you sleep-y _ head. _

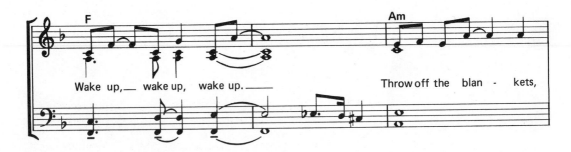

Wake up, _ wake up, wake up. _ Throw off the blan - kets,

rub your _ eyes, _ To - day is a spec - ial day.

There's gon - na be _ a big sur - prise _ head-ing your way, _

Come on and play, _ Wake up, _ wake up, wake up, _ wake up, _ wake up, wake _

up. Wake up, wake up, wake — up (Shout) WAKE UP.

Light up Diwali

Sandra Kerr

1. Light up Di-wa-li, Fire-works and can-dles are burn-ing, Wel-come the trav-eller re-turn-ing, Light up Di-wa-li. Di-

Fine Chorus

— wa-li to har-vest the sum-mer. Di-wa-li to Ra-ma and Si-ta. Di-wa-li to bring in the New Year. Di-

— wa-li to bright-en the fu-ture.

2. Dance for Diwali,
Telling old stories and singing,
Presents and parties we're giving,
Dance for Diwali.

Chorus

3. Colour Diwali,
Fresh in the new clothes we're wearing,
Bright in the patterns we're weaving,
Colour Diwali.

Chorus

4. Welcome Diwali,
Farmers sow seed for the winter,
Families grow closer together,
Welcome Diwali.

Chorus

Harvest

Peter Morrell

Har - vest, har - vest   H A R V

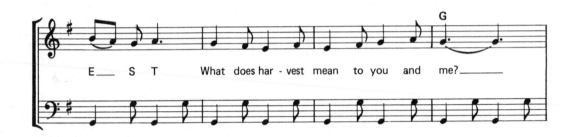

E ___ S T   What does har - vest mean to you and me? ___

Look a-round the world ___ and see   what the har - vest

means to you and me ___   1. H is for the
2. E is for the

hedge-rows with their har - vest fruit ___ A for all the ap - ples from the
en - er - gy the far - mer's need ___ S for slip- 'ry fish straight from the

trees ____   R is rice that's grown in pad - dy
sea ____   T is thanks we give when all is

fields ____ a - far ____   V for ev' - ry veg - e - ta - ble
ga - thered in ____ Thanks to all the har - vest - ers from

brown ____ white ____ green ____   *f*   At har - vest
you ____ and ____ me ____

CODA

time (clap, clap)   me ____   *ff* *(shouted)* It's har - vest time!

Thread of my dreams

Ann Bryant

Calmly and slowly

mp 1. Soft as a whis-per the mist of the dawn As I o-pen my eyes to a-no-ther new day. Si-lent and still in the world so it seems Gent-ly I tread on the thread of my dreams. Sum-mer is slip-ping and *(dim. to end)*

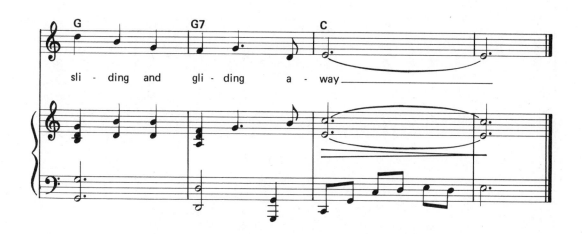

sli - ding and gli - ding a - way

2. Gossamer cobwebs are heavy with dew,
Soft falling leaves but there's no other sound,
Dead and laid bare is the earth so it seems,
Gently I tread on the thread of my dreams,
Yes, there are stories to tell from the world underground.

3. Seeds that were sown long ago in the deep
Are the Harvest of flowers and fruit for today,
Beauty and colour abound so it seems,
Gently I tread on the thread of my dreams,
Safely we gather together and 'Thank you' we say.

All sorts of people

Clive Barnwell

1. Thank you, Lord, for the
Thank you, Lord, for the

sun that shines And the rain that falls on the coun - try - side, That
wind that blows That takes the leaves so the fruit tree grows, That

4th time only repeat 3 times

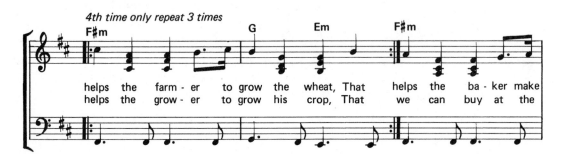

helps the farm - er to grow the wheat, That helps the ba - ker make
helps the grow - er to grow his crop, That we can buy at the

bread to eat. lo - cal shop. There's all sorts of peo - ple In

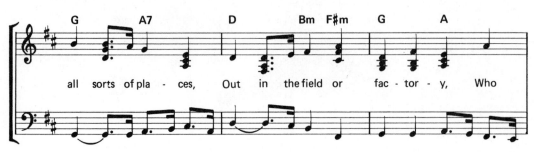

all sorts of pla - ces, Out in the field or fac - tor - y, Who

grow   or   pre-pare   or   pack food in ca - ses,   So   that when I   get

home,   there's   tea.

2. Thank you, Lord, for the snow we see
That melts in rivers that reach the sea,
Which holds the food that the fish will get
That helps the fisherman fill his net.

Thank you, Lord, for the rocks and soil
That men drill down through to get the oil,
That helps the farmer to plough his field,
That helps the grower to move his yield,
That helps the fishermen out at sea
And brings their harvest to you and me.

Chorus

Winter rock

Gillian Parker

Steady rock beat

f 1. The clocks go back, the days grow cold, The birds don't sing and the year is old. The garden dies, the trees are bare, The chill of winter fills — the air. The hedge-hog and the squir-rel sleep, Be -

2.Now in that world of ice and sleet,
Of winter sunshine, thin and weak,
Of heavy clouds and falling snow,
Of ghostly moonlight shining below,
We wake up early, rush outside –
On snow and ice we skid and slide
And make our way to the park beyond
Where the ducks learn to skate on the
  frozen pond.

3.Now in that pond the fish swim deep
Beneath the ice in their winter sleep.
Their shadows lurking in the weed,
Too tired to swim, too tired to feed.
While we all dance and sing and play
And make our plans for Christmas day
As we go to market to buy a tree
And hang it round with tinsel for all to
  see.

Hanukka candles

David Moses

1. One in the cen - tre one on the right, Can - dles in the win - dows, more each night. Sha-mash, the ser - vant light - ing the rest, Han - uk - ka can - dles, bright and blessed.

Chorus Han - uk - ka _____ a great thanks - giv- ing and Han - uk - ka _____ a brand new start Fil - ling us _____ with the joy of liv - ing and the Light that shines from a lov - ing heart.

2.Songs to be sung and prayers to be prayed,
Presents to be given and games to be played.
Spinning the dreidel, where will it stop?
Half, all or nothing on the spinning of a top.

Chorus

3.Blessings recited, tales to be read
Of battles that were fought and blood that was shed.
Saving the Temple, making it fit
For the oil in the Lamp of the Lord to be lit.

Chorus

4.Wine to be tasted, food to be shared,
Fresh potato pancakes to be prepared.
Being together, family and friends,
Hanukka gelt for children to spend.

Chorus

5.Lit from the centre, added from the right,
Eight Hanukka candles burning bright.
Shamash, the servant, that makes nine
Blazing their message 'til the end of time.

Chorus

Christmas at school

Music by Debbie Campbell and words by Jacqui Dillon

f

Loud, stomping

1. Teach - er's cross and got the hump. The

class - room's like a rub - bish dump. There's glit - ter here and

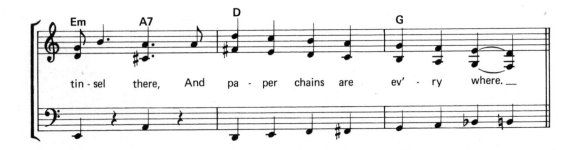

tin - sel there, And pa - per chains are ev' - ry where. __

Chorus

ff Christ - mas is here and it's on - ly No - vem - ber.

Christ - mas at school we will al - ways re - mem - ber

Ringing

ff Christ - mas is here and it's on - ly No - vem - ber.

Christ - mas at school we will al - ways re - mem - ber.

2.Joseph's wearing his dad's dressing gown
And Mary's socks keep falling down.
The angel's wings have gone all funny,
And one of the shepherds' nose is runny.

Chorus

3.I've done my card all back to front,
My coloured pencils have gone all blunt,
The dye's coming out of my crêpe paper hat,
And I haven't even made my party mat.

Chorus

Christmas eve

Gillian Parker

(Sleigh bells)

D
I hear sleigh bells jing - ling, jing - ling,

Rein - deer hoofs a gal - lop - ing, gal - lop - ing, **A7** In the dis - tance

jing - ling, gal - lop - ing, Com - ing near - er jing - ling, gal - lop - ing,

D Sets my spine a - ting - ling, ting - ling, **G** On the frost - y

night air ring - a - ling, **A** Shut my eyes so tight and wish and

D wish that they were here. **A** In the **D** dark - ness jing - ling, jing - ling,

Sleigh bells soft - ter, van - ish - ing, van - ish - ing in the dark.

Ring bells, ring

David Moses

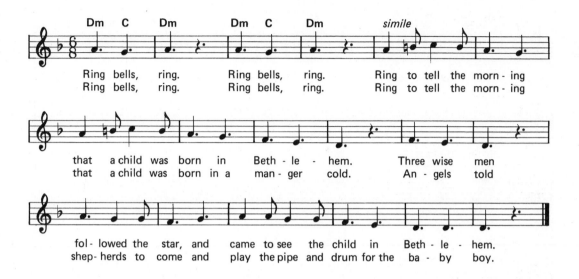

Ring bells, ring. Ring bells, ring. Ring to tell the morn - ing
Ring bells, ring. Ring bells, ring. Ring to tell the morn - ing

that a child was born in Beth - le - hem. Three wise men
that a child was born in a man - ger cold. An - gels told

fol - lowed the star, and came to see the child in Beth - le - hem.
shep - herds to come and play the pipe and drum for the ba - by boy.

Our Christmas prayer

Gerald Haigh

Our Christ-mas prayer this year While our lives are mer-ry and bright, Is for a

world that's free from fear And that we'll turn to the stars' pure light.

2. Our Christmas prayer for you
As you join with us in our song,
Is that the Christ-child comes anew
Into your hearts the whole year long.

3. Our Christmas prayer dear friends
Is for loved ones far away,
Each loving message that we send
Will bring them close on Christmas day.

Tell it to the world

Lesley Funge

Tell it to the East, Tell it to the West, Tell it to the South and Nor - th, Tell it to the poles, Tell it round the world, Let the mes - sage go forth, Shout it from the roof - tops to the earth be - low,___ Shout it to the peo - ple___ where - ev - er you go,___ Je - sus___ is born___ for the whole wide world. ___

Chorus

2. Jesus, we bring you all our presents,
Symbols of hearts so full of love.
Watch how the Kings give gold, myrrh, incense,
Gifts for a babe from God above.

Chorus

3. Jesus, today the world rejoices,
Peace and happiness we share.
Here, there are no more angry voices,
Safe from a world that will not care.

Chorus

Circle of love

Music by Leonora and Elena Davies and words by Leonora Davies

Not too fast

1. Let's

join hands (let's join hands) And join hearts (and join hearts) and

join our minds a-cross the big di-vide _____ Of

na-tions (of na-tions) and peo-ples (and peo-ples) And

make a cir-cle of love a-round the year. _____

It's time to cel - e - brate, time to shout a - bout, Time to dance a - bout,

time to sing a - bout, Time to hope a - bout, time to think a - bout

Slower

Lov - ing each and ev - ery - one. 2. At

2. At Christmas, Diwali,
Whatever time of year it might be,
On birthdays or feast days
Let's make a circle of love around the year.
With time to celebrate, time to shout about,
Time to dance about, time to sing about,
Time to hope about, time to think about,
Loving each and every one.

(Repeat verse 1 to fine.)

There go our festivals

Peter Morrell

F
Gm
p
There go our fes - ti - vals.
Eb
Eb F
F
mf
p
All thro' the year there is one that's so near we can ce - le - brate. They're worth re -
Gm
Eb
mf
- mem - ber - ing Think - ing of times gone by. Ask - ing the ques - tion why
C7
Bb
F
Bb
F
f
does time fly by? So ends the year Mem - 'ries so clear...
Bb
F A7 Dm
Bb
All that there's left to do Now we've seen them thro' is to
C7
F
Faug
F
Faug
mf
say to you... Good - bye, good - bye, good - bye, good - bye.
F
Faug
F
Faug rall.
F
Good - bye sim. good-bye.
pp
Good - bye, good-bye, good-bye, good-bye, good-bye, good-bye, good-bye, good-bye, good-bye.
pp
Good-bye sim.

ME AND MY WORLD

David Moses

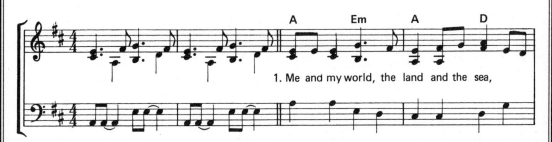

1. Me and my world, the land and the sea,

Stars in the sky, leaves on a tree. My world, you could see or smell or

Chorus

hear it, My world, you could touch it when you're near it, My world.

2. Me and my world, the people I know,
Things that I see, places I go.

Chorus

3. Me and my world, good thing to eat,
Hair on my head, toes on my feet.

Chorus

4. Me and my world, the place where I stay,
Coming back home, going away.

Chorus

5. Me and my world, the dark and the light,
Make me feel safe or give me a fright.

Chorus

6. Me and my world, people who care,
Gifts I can give, things I can share.

photocopiable

At the ripe old age of one

David Moses

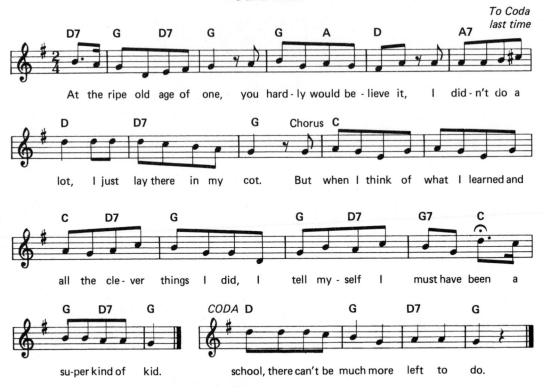

At the ripe old age of one, you hard-ly would be-lieve it, I did-n't do a
lot, I just lay there in my cot. But when I think of what I learned and
all the cle-ver things I did, I tell my-self I must have been a
su-per kind of kid.
school, there can't be much more left to do.

2.At the ripe old age of two, you hardly would believe it,
I first began to walk, and then I learned to talk.

Chorus

3.At the ripe old age of three, you hardly would believe it,
I had a lovely time when I learned to run and climb.

Chorus

4.At the ripe old age of four, you hardly would believe it,
I had a friend called Mike and I learned to ride a bike.

Chorus

5.At the ripe old age of five, you hardly would believe it,
I paddled in a pool and began to go to school.

Chorus

6.At the ripe old age of six, you hardly would believe it,
I learned to fly a kite and began to read and write.

Chorus

7.At the ripe old age of seven, you hardly would believe it,
I could jump across a brook and add numbers in a book.

Chorus

8.At the ripe old age of eight, you hardly would believe it,
I learned to roller skate and I sometimes stayed up late.

Chorus

9.At the ripe old age of nine, you hardly would believe it,
I learned to light a fire and mend a puncture in my tyre.

Chorus

10.At the ripe old age of ten, you hardly would believe it,
We learn so much at school,
There can't be much more left to do.

What Annie McRae wanted for tea

Ann Bryant

2. At six years old Annie McRae had pancakes for
     tea every day.
So when it was teatime her mother would say,
'How many pancakes do you want today?'

Said Annie,
'One for the video of Winnie the Pooh,
Two for ice cream and three lots of snow,
Four for a midnight feast with Lizzie and Sue,
Five to have hair that could magically grow.'

3. At seven years old Annie McRae had cherries for
     tea every day.
So when it was teatime her mother would say,
'How many cherries do you want today?'

Said Annie,
'One for my family and all of my friends,
Two to be kind and three to be true,
Four to be healthy and to never tell lies,
Five you love me ... and six I love you.'

Scratch my tummy like a chimpanzee

David Moses

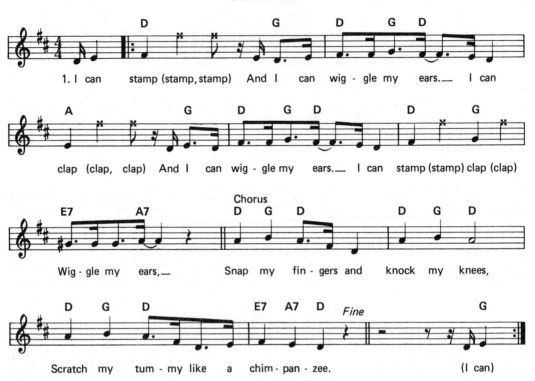

1. I can stamp (stamp, stamp) And I can wig-gle my ears.— I can clap (clap, clap) And I can wig-gle my ears.— I can stamp (stamp) clap (clap)

Chorus

Wig-gle my ears,— Snap my fin-gers and knock my knees, Scratch my tum-my like a chim-pan-zee. (I can)

2. I can hop (hop hop)
And I can wobble my nose.
I can wave (wave wave)
And I can wobble my nose.
I can hop (hop) wave (wave)
Wobble my nose.

Chorus

3. I can hoot (toot toot)
And I can bend my arms.
I can kiss (kiss kiss)
And I can bend my arms.
I can hoot (toot) kiss (kiss)
Bend my arms.

Chorus

4. I can bang (boom boom)
And I can ring on a bell.
I can crash (crash crash)
And I can ring on a bell.
I can bang (boom) crash (crash)
Ring on a bell.

Chorus

It's never the time or place

Howard Skempton

1. It's no bad thing to skip and shout. It's no bad thing to

fall a - bout. But when I want to sing, they bawl me out For it's

ne-ver the time or place It's place Ne-ver the time or place.

2. It's no bad thing to lie in wait.
It's no bad thing to climb a gate.
But when I want to sing they get irate,
For it's never the time or place.

3. It's no bad thing to stay up late.
It's no bad thing to prattle and prate.
But when I want to sing they get in a state,
For it's never the time or place.

4. It's no bad thing to break a lace.
It's no bad thing to lose a race.
But when I want to sing they pull a face,
For it's never the time or place *(repeat)*.

I know they're bad for my teeth

David Moses

just have a - no-ther lit - tle sweet.   *(sigh)* BANANA

2. I know they're bad for my teeth,
And they're made of dreadful stuff,
But I like toffee and walnut whips,
I just can't get enough.

Chorus

3. I know they're bad for my teeth,
They'll bring me out in a blotch,
But I like rock and sherbet dabs,
Boiled sweets and butterscotch.

Chorus

4. I know they're bad for my teeth,
They'll rot and all drop out,
And though I like those sweet, sticky things,
There really is no doubt that...

Chorus

Apples and bananas

Arranged by Mike Fenton (trad. American)

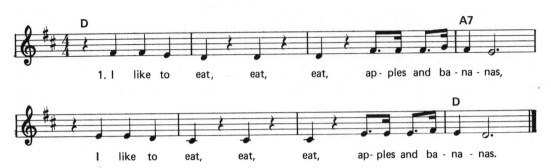

1. I like to eat, eat, eat, ap-ples and ba-na-nas,

I like to eat, eat, eat, ap-ples and ba-na-nas.

A simple little song which takes on a very humorous slant when the vowels of the alphabet are substituted in the words 'eat', 'apples' and 'bananas'. Take the vowels in order, (a,e,i,o,u) so that the second verse becomes:

'I like to aat, aat, aat, apples and bananas', etc.

Verse 3 – 'I like to eat, eat, eat, epples and benenes', etc.

Verse 4 – 'I like to iat, iat, iat, ipples and bininis', etc.

Children soon become experts. Try it then with 'Pepperoni Pizza' or 'Taramasalata'. There are infinite variations!

What are you wearing?

Jane Morgan

Make up your own extra verses to the song. Here are some suggestions:

I'm wearing a stetson/coolie hat/sun-hat because it keeps me cool.
I'm wearing a bath hat because it keeps me dry.
I'm wearing a crash hat/fireman's hat because it keeps me safe.

You're smiling

Leonora Davies

1. Look in the mir - ror __ and what do you see? __ I see a fun - ny face __

look - ing at me. __ Turn up your nose __ and wrink - le your eyes. __

Give your - self a __ big __ sur - prise, Be - cause you're smil - ing __

smil - ing __ Smil-ing makes you feel good __ in - side Be-cause you're

smil - ing __ smil - ing And feel - ing good __ in - side.

2.Out in the world with strangers you meet,
Look at their faces and not at their feet.
Turn up your nose and wrinkle your eyes,
Give the world a big surprise.
Because you're spreading your smiling,
Helping the world to feel good inside,
Because you're spreading your smiling,
The world feels good inside.

3.Turn to a friend and what do you see?
I see a funny face looking at me.
Turn up your nose and wrinkle your eyes,
Give your friend a big surprise.
Because you're sharing your smiling,
Both of you now feel good inside,
Because you're sharing your smiling
And feeling good inside.

Mum! Mum! Quickly come

Ann Bryant

Steady, rhythmic

1. I saw a gi-ant on the wall. It stood there fif-ty me-tres tall. It made me feel so ve-ry small. It was a gi-ant on__ the

Chorus

wall, so I called, 'Mum! Mum! quick-ly come,__I'm not stay-ing here on my own. Mum! Mum! quick-ly come,__ Some-thing tells me I am not a-lone.' -lone.'

8ve___

2.I saw a bundle of fur in the air,
It growled at me like a grizzly bear.
It fixed me with a beady stare,
You know you mustn't stare at a bear, so I called...

Chorus

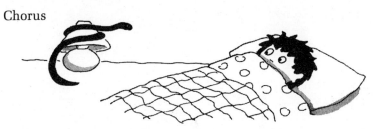

3.I saw a snake hanging from the light,
It hissed at me, 'Mind the bugs don't bite'.
My goose bumps bumped and my face went white,
It was a snake hanging from the light, so I called...

Chorus

4.I saw a bee on my pillow case,
It made a beeline for my face.
It gave my heartbeat quite a race,
It was a bee on my pillow case, so I called...

Chorus

5.I saw a mouse scuttle under my bed,
'Eek eek, squeak squeak, nibble nibble,' it said.
'I'm only here for a piece of cheese.
Don't call your mum, oh please don't, please!'
So I yelled...

Chorus

Goodness how you've grown

Veronica Clark

1. When - ev - er Gran - ny Need - ham comes, she pats me on the head,

Smo - thers me with kis - ses 'til I wish that I were dead. ___ Says

'Good - ness gra - cious me child, how the time has flown, ___ Since

last I came to see you, you have grown and grown and grown!'

Chorus

Oh Gran - ny Need - ham, what - ev - er would you think, If in -

- stead of get - ting tal - ler, I would shrink and shrink and shrink?

Last line of last verse

Oh Gran - dad, you're a smash - er and I like you such a lot.

ral. . . . . end

2.Whenever Uncle Harry comes he slaps me on the back,
Swings me round and throws me up, then dumps me like a sack.
Says, 'Goodness gracious me child, how the time has flown,
Since last I came to see you, you have grown and grown and grown!'

Chorus
Oh Uncle Harry...

3.Whenever Auntie Dolly comes she ruffles up my hair,
Gazes at me lovingly, then hugs me like a bear.
Says, 'Goodness gracious me child, how the time has flown,
Since last I came to see you, you have grown and grown and grown!'

Chorus
Oh Auntie Dolly...

4.Whenever Grandad Rowley comes he shakes me by the hand,
Slips me 50p and says, 'Hello, you're looking grand.
It's very nice to see you, you haven't changed a jot.'
Oh Grandad, you're a smasher and I like you such a lot!

F.R.I.E.N.D.S.

Peter Morrell

2. Friends will always help you out
Even when you want to scream and shout,
Friends will often go without
Then you're never in doubt. (So always try to)

Chorus

3. Friends are happy to be there
When you're feeling blue and you don't care,
Friends will always go half share
And you know they'll be fair! (So always try to)

Chorus

4. All around the world let's send
Friendly messages that never end,
Then perhaps we'll start a trend
And the world will be friends. (So always try to)

Chorus

My friend Billy loves bubble gum

David Moses

2.My friend Jillie loves bubble gum, bubble gum,
Gonna go to town and get her some, get her some.
My friend Jillie loves bubble gum, bubble gum,
Gonna go to town and get her some, get her some.
Yellow bubble gum, sweet as honey,
Blue bubble gum, tastes real funny,
Pink bubble gum, great for blowing,
Like a balloon, it just keeps growing.

3.Jillie and Billy love bubble gum, bubble gum,
Gonna go to town and get 'em some, get 'em some.
Jillie and Billy love bubble gum, bubble gum,
Gonna go to town and get 'em some, get 'em some.

My pets

Gillian Parker

Make up your own animals, sounds and food.

Doctor, Doctor

David Moses

1. Doc - tor, Doc - tor, help me do, I feel a lit - tle

sick, and I don't want to. Give me a pow - der, give me a

pill. Hur - ry, hur - ry Doc - tor, 'cause I do feel ill.

2. Nurse, Nurse, help me please,
I've got a little cough,
I've got a little sneeze.
I got soaked, I think I caught a chill.
Hurry, hurry Nurse, 'cause I do feel ill.

3. Please Mr Dentist, don't hang about,
I ate too many sweets and
My teeth are dropping out.
Give them a polish with your high speed drill.
Hurry Mr Dentist, 'cause I do feel ill.

Our school cook

David Moses

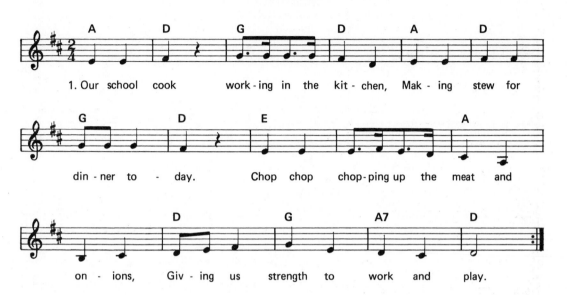

1. Our school cook working in the kit-chen, Mak-ing stew for din-ner to - day. Chop chop chop-ping up the meat and on - ions, Giv-ing us strength to work and play.

2.Our school cook, working in the kitchen,
Making pie for dinner today.
Rolling, rolling out the pastry crust,
Giving us strength to work and play.

3.Our school cook, working in the kitchen,
Making fish and chips for dinner today.
Shaking, shaking up the chips in the chip pan,
Giving us the strength to work and play.

4.Our school cook, working in the kitchen,
Making cake for pudding today.
Stirring, stirring up the milk and flour,
Giving us strength to work and play.

Say 'Thanks'

Gillian Parker

1. Who helps us cross ov-er the road? It's the lol - ly-pop man. Who helps us when we are lost? It's the police - man. Who helps us when we trip and fall down? Who helps us smile when we're try - ing to frown?__ It's our bro - thers and our sis - ters and our

un - cles, aunts and grans, Say, 'Thanks,' Say, 'Thanks,' Say,

'Thanks,' to the peo - ple who help us.

2. Who helps us learn wrong from right?
It's our mother.
Who helps us learn to share?
It's our brother.
Who helps us when we're tired and sad?
Who loves us even when we're being bad?
There is no one else who helps us like our mums and dads.
Say 'Thanks',
Say 'Thanks',
Say 'Thanks', to the people who love us.

Mrs Govinder Singh

David Moses

Mis-sus Go-vin-der Singh had a lit-tle shop with a

roof on top, peo-ple come out and in.

What shall we buy? Why not try tea from In-di-a

1
ve-ry ve-ry nice. San-dal-wood per-fume (breathe in)

2
aaaaah, tea from In-di-a, ve-ry ve-ry nice.

3
Chic-ken bi-ri-a-ni mmmmmm,

San-dal-wood per-fume (breathe in) aaaaah, tea from In-di-a

4
ve-ry ve-ry nice. In-di-an mu-sic

ti-ka-ti-ka-ta ti-ka-ti-ka-ta ti-ka-ti-ka-ta ti-ka-ti-ka-ta

Chic-ken bi-ri-a-ni mmmmm,_____ San-dal-wood per-fume.

(breathe in) aaaaah, tea from In-di-a, ve-ry ve-ry nice.

Going round the fair

Ian Henderson Begg

1. Driv - ing round the dod - gems, Crash - ing in - to some,

Stamp - ing on the ped - als, Hang - ing on to Mum.

Chorus

Go - ing round the fair, Go - ing round the fair,

Flash - ing lights and mu - sic, All a - round the fair.

2. On the roller-coaster,
Going round so fast,
Hang onto the handles,
Wind is rushing past.

Chorus

3. Down the helter-skelter
On a tickly mat,
Round and round the outside
Of a wizard's hat.

Chorus

4. Swinging in the cages
As the wheel goes round,
Look at all the people
Down upon the ground.

Chorus

5. Try to win a teddy
Catch a plastic duck,
Look, she's won a goldfish
How is that for luck!

Chorus

6. Crowds of happy people
Excitement fills the air,
Dad says it's expensive
Going to the fair.

Chorus

Colours

Ann Bryant

col - ours spar-kle, Col - ours glit-ter and col-ours gleam, Fast a-sleep with your

eyes tight shut, You can still see the col - ours you dream.

2.Colours whisper soft and secret,
Colours float on the smallest prayer,
Colours clash in the storm outside
And the sparks fly around in the air.

Yellow is summer, shining and golden,
Silver is sparkling water icy cold.
Purple is plums and pink is for piglets,
Castles and kings are gold.

Dream of colours, rainbow colours,
Dancing flowers in a world so grey,
Light and bright colours, dusk and dark
Till the dawn brings the colours of day.

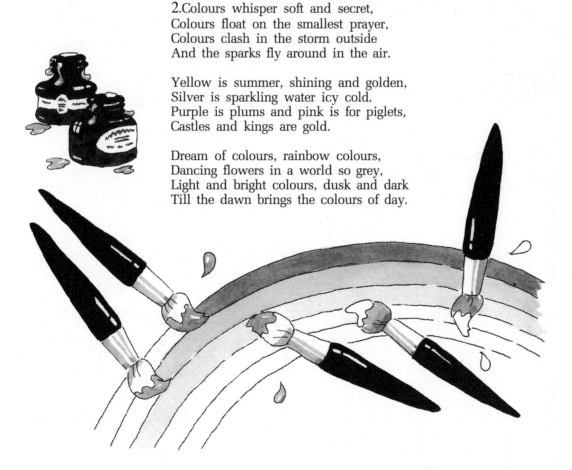

One world family

Peter Morrell

Giving and getting

David Moses

Give ____ a lit-tle joy, give ____ a lit-tle love.

Give ____ a lit-tle help to those ____ who ne-ver have e-

-nough. Give ____ a lit-tle hap-pi-ness, ____ give ____ a lit-tle smile.

Get-ting can be fun, but giv-ing can be more worth-while.

THE WORLD WE LIVE IN

Peter Morrell

1. The world we live in is a beau-ti-ful place, It's full of beau-ty for the hu-man race. But it's a fact much more than that, Our world of beau-ty forms a spe-cial ha-bi-tat __ For the crea-tures of the air, the crea-tures of the sea, The crea-tures of the coun-try-side, the plants and the trees, __ Yes the world we live in is a it's a beau-ti-ful beau-ti-ful place.

See the world

Gillian Parker

It's so ea-sy to see the world, Cross the sea, cross the land by ae-ro-plane, Fly-ing back-wards and for-wards in time, All a-round the globe and back a-gain back a- gain, back a- gain.

1. Vis - it France, vis - it Spain, vis - it I - ta - ly, vis - it

Chorus

2. Visit Iceland, visit Greenland, visit Canada,
Visit China, visit Hong Kong, visit Sri Lanka,
Visit Togo, visit Norway, visit Jamaica
And if you've got the time, see Australia.

Chorus

3. See the Wonders of the World, see the Taj Mahal,
Visit Katmandu, the Himalayas and Nepal.
If you get as far as China, walk on the Great Wall
And if you've got the time, see Niagara Falls.

Chorus

International Brother John

Arrangement by Mike Fenton

① F (C7) F   ② F   F

Are you sleep - ing? Are you sleep - ing? Bro - ther John,

③ F

Bro - ther John, Morn - ing bells are ring - ing,

④ F C7 F

Morn-ing bells are ring - ing, Ding Dang Dong. Ding Dang Dong.

Fray Felipé (Spanish)	Frère Jacques (French)
Duermes tú	Dormez-vous?
Toque la campaña	Sonnez les matines
Tin Tan Ton	Din Don Din
Schlafen Sie (German)	Jam Jay Yo (Korean)
Bruder Hans	John Hyung a
Morgenglocken läuten	Ah chim jonge oolinae
Bim Bam Bim	Ding Ding Ding
Doy hoy mung chung (Chinese – a US/	A-chi-noo ya-a-kov (Hebrew)
Ya jak Moon Cantonese var.)	Al Ti-shan
Fee die loin by see may	Ha-pa-a-mon me-tsal-tsel
Din Don Din	Bim Bam Bam
Wy't ti'n cysgu (Welsh)	Kay Tko Suta Paya (Punjabi)
Ioan, frowd	Bhai John
Clychaur bore'n canu	Suba Ghanti Bajti Hay
Ding Dang Dong	Ding Dang Dong
Faden Jacob (Dutch)	Chayvay spee chay (Polish)
Staapt hi noch	Bratchay Jan
Ahle clocke liden	Szitskay Zronay Beong
Ding Dang Dong	Ding Dang Dong

Mike Fenton, the internationally known autoharp player, has collected many verses for this well-loved traditional tune which can, of course, be sung as a round.

Toc toc toc

Ann Bryant

Toc toc toc! Qui est là? *(Bird or animal noise)*

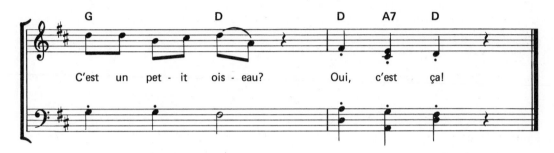

C'est un pet-it ois-eau? Oui, c'est ça!

2.Knock knock knock
Who is there? *(Noise)*
Is it a little bird?
Yes it is.

Continue with any number of verses substituting the following
birds/animals for 'oiseau':   mouton — sheep
vache – cow
cochon – pig
canard – duck
poulet – chicken
souris – mouse
pony – pony
etc.

Last verse: Child's name. Choose a child who says 'Bonjour' and
the other children must then guess who it was.

Life in the sun

Ann Bryant

1. If you lived in a cave, in the dark un-der-ground Where the day-light can't come in, There'd be no-thing to see and ne-ver a sound. You could ea-si-ly hear a pin drop, PING! No, it can't be much fun like our life in the sun, We are luc-ky to live in the

coun - try. No, it can't be much fun, — like our

life in the sun. — We are luc - ky to live — in — the

coun - try. If you coun - try.

2. If you lived in the town with the noise all around,
There'd be never a sign of green.
You'd see someone you know and you'd call out 'hello',
But you wouldn't be heard or seen, HELLO!

Chorus

3. If you lived in a boat where it's wet all around,
You'd make everything water tight.
You'd keep moving all day and you'd still seem to sway
When you're trying to sleep at night time, OH!

Chorus

People for peace

Peter Morrell

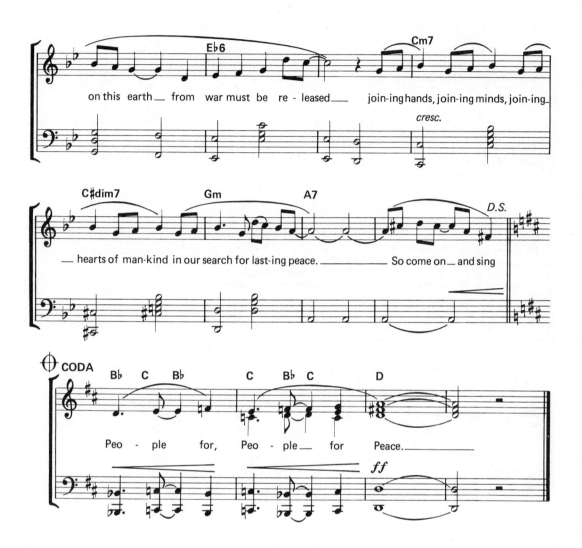

2. People for Peace, and peace for ev'ryone (People for Peace).
All around this world of ours there are People for Peace.
Ev'ry person on this earth has got a part to play,
Ev'ry person on this earth has something good to say,
Ev'ry person on this earth has got to find a way –
Joining hands, joining minds, joining hearts of mankind
In our search of peace today,
So come and sing, People for, People for Peace.

3. People for Peace, and peace for ev'ryone (People for Peace).
All around this world of ours there are People for Peace.
When we work together we will see the mountains move,
When we work together we'll see sky that's always blue,
When we work together we will see what we can do –
Joining hands, joining minds, joining hearts of mankind
In our search for peace and truth,
So come and sing, People for, People for Peace.

The whale

Clive Barnwell

Swim-ming a - long quite hap - pi - ly. Should I catch him or let him be free? The way a whale should be. be in the sea. Hap-pi-ly swim-ming free.

2. Whales are most important things to industry,
But it's more important still
That there's whales in the sea.
Will the whales all go before we really know?

Perhaps I'll never see one till the day I die,
But it's nice to know they're there
If I should care to try.
How long will there be real whales in the
Bright, blue ocean?

Chorus

Lonely panda waltz

Debbie Campbell

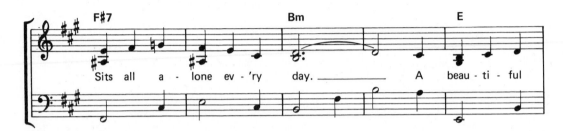

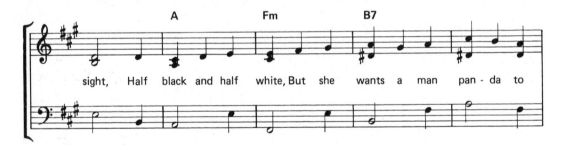

2. With nothing to do
But chew on bamboo
And snooze for a while on the ground,
It's so hard to find
A man of her kind
When there just aren't that many around
To be found,
There just aren't that many around.

3. We mustn't neglect her,
We'll try to protect her,
The message is perfectly clear.
We'll find her a mate
Before it's too late
Or pandas may all disappear
I fear,
Or pandas may all disappear.

Bounce kangaroo bounce

Mike Fenton

Bouncily

1. Wish I had me a kan-ga-roo From the out-back of Aus-tra-lia___

Leap-in' a-round he's a real ath-lete At bounc-in' he's no fail-ure. ___

Chorus

Bounce kan-ga-roo bo-unce ___ *(group repeats)*)

You've got so much po-wer.___ *(group repeats)*)

Leap-in' a-bout on those great hind legs___ *(group repeats)* At

thir-ty miles an ho-ur.___ (At thir-ty miles an ho-ur.)___

2. A kangaroo can crop the lawn
And give you fun and laughter,
But you're gonna need a high, high fence
And who will clean up after?

Chorus

3. With a great long tail and baby pouch,
Big appetite please pardon,
A vegetarian like that
Will eat the whole back garden.

Chorus

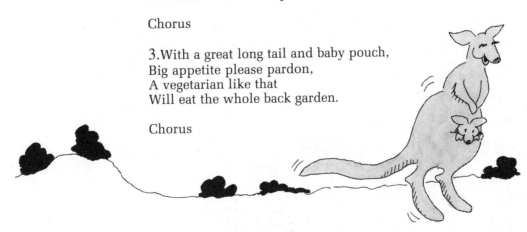

The camel has got the hump

David Moses

cam - el was cros - sing the des - ert   Lum - pi - ty thum - pi - ty

bump.   His   back   was   sore,   life   was   a   bore, and   the
The

cam - el had got   the hump.   A   feet   were   flat   (pat knees)   he'd

lost   his   hat   (pat head)   his   back   was   sore,   life   was   a bore, and the

cam - el had got   the hump.   A   sand   was   rough   (rub hands   and he'd
together)

quite   had e - nough   (fold arms) his   feet   were   flat   (pat knees)   he'd

lost his hat (pat head) his back was sore, life was a bore, and the

cam-el had got the hump. A cam-el was cros-sing the des-ert

lum-pi-ty thum-pi-ty bump His eyes blinked (blink eyes) he

want-ed a drink (tongue out) The sand was rough (rub hands together) and he'd

had quite e-nough (fold arms) his feet were flat (pat knees) he'd

lost his hat (pat head) his back was sore,

life was a bore, and the cam-el had got the hump.

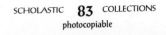

The orangutang song

David Moses

Samba rhythm

F(C) *   **C(G)**   **C(G)**   **F(C)**

It's fun to go to the zoo, There's lots to see and do

1. A
2.

D7(A7)   **Gm(Dm)**   **G7(D7)**

pan - ther's fur is shi - ny black. Look at the ze - bra's
Pen - guin's wad - dle from side to side. You can ev - en go for an

C7(G7)   **F(C)**   **C(G)**   **C7(G7)**

stri - py back. Some are fierce and wild, o - thers are meek and
el - e - phant ride. Some are ter - ri - bly tall, o - thers are ti - ny and

F(C)   **C7(G7)**   **C(G)**   **G7(D7)**

mild. But of all the an - i - mals I love best, one stands out a -
small.

C(G7)   **C7(G7)**   Chorus   **F(C)**

- bove the rest. O - rang - u - tang your coat is

The world we live in

o - rang - ey-brown, O-rang-u-tang your arms are long and hang down.

When you walk it makes me grin, but how you can climb and jump and swing.

O - rang - u - tang your face is

fun - ny and flat, O-rang-u-tang your tum's a lit-tle bit fat.

So ma-ny cle-ver things you can do. O-rang-u-tang I love you.

* Guitarists put capo on 5th fret and play bracketed chords.

Owl can't get to sleep

Ann Bryant

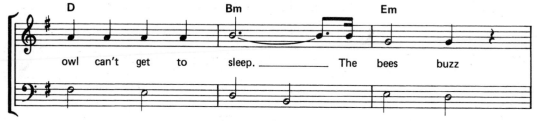

2. It's day time in the great big wood, but the owl can't get to sleep.
The squirrel cracks nuts, CRACK CRACK CRACK and the owl can't get to sleep.

3. It's day time in the great big wood, but the owl can't get to sleep.
The woodpecker pecks, PECK PECK PECK and the owl can't get to sleep.

4. It's night time in the great big wood, but the birds can't get to sleep.
The owl screeches, T-WIT T-WOOOO! and the birds can't get to sleep.

This song is based on the story 'Goodnight Owl' by Pat Hutchins.

Chicks grow into chickens

David Moses

1. Chicks grow in - to chic - kens, Calves grow in - to cows. Sy - ca - more seeds grow in - to trees, _____ but Cubs grow in - to lions and ti - gers, Bad - gers, fox - es, Leo - pards and wolves and bears.

2.Foals grow into horses,
Kittens grow into cats.
Fresh green shoots grow out of roots, but
Cubs grow into lions and tigers,
Badgers, foxes,
Leopards and wolves and bears.

3.Pups grow into seals or dogs,
Lambs grow into sheep.
Bulbs can grow into daffodils, but
Cubs grow into lions and tigers,
Badgers, foxes,
Leopards and wolves and bears.

Eeny meeny minibeasts

David Moses

Ee - ny mee - ny mi - ni - beasts, Fat or skin - ny beasts,

Spi - ders lurk - ing, Ants hard work - ing, Hop - ping, hur - ry - ing,

Crawl - ing, scur - ry - ing, Wrig - gl - y, squig - gl - y

mi - ni - beasts. 1. Beet - les, bats and bees, Drag - on - flies and

fleas, Glid - ing, glit - ter - ing, Float - ing, flit - ter - ing,

Bum - bl - y, tum - bl - y mi - ni - beasts.

Chorus

2. Ladybirds and bugs,
Centipedes and slugs,
Sliding, slithering,
Diving, dithering,
Racketty, clacketty minibeasts.

Chorus

3. Woodlice, worms and wasps,
Millipedes and moths,
Hard and hovery,
Biting, bothery,
Buzzery, whuzzery minibeasts.

Chorus

4. Newts and water snails,
Tadpoles with long tails,
Swish and swimmering,
Shy and shimmering,
Speckledy, freckledy minibeasts.

Chorus

Eighteen spiders

David Moses

1. Eight - een spi - ders, ev - er so small, You'd hard - ly know they were spi - ders at all.

Chorus
Eight - een spi - ders, rea - dy and keen, The mem-bers of the Spi - ders Sky Dive Team.

2. They all climb up an old tree trunk,
One gives the order, and off they jump.

Chorus

3. Floating feet above the ground,
They all join hands and circle round.

Chorus

4. Just inches above the grass below,
They break the circle and off they go.

Chorus

5. Those daring spiders feel no dread,
They all land safe on a spider's web.
The bravest sight you've ever seen,
The members of the Spiders Sky Dive Team.

Caterpillar lullaby

Debbie Campbell

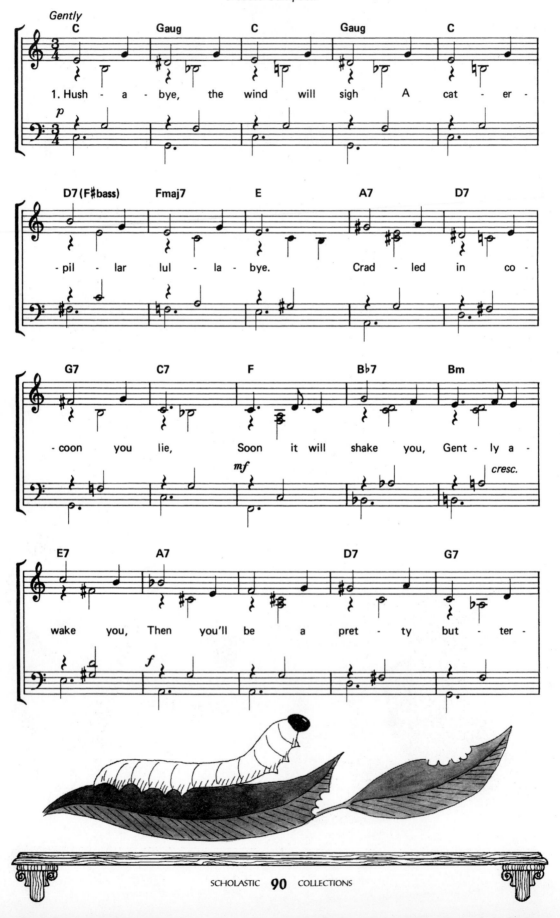

1. Hush - a - bye, the wind will sigh A cat - er - pil - lar lul - la - bye. Crad - led in co - coon you lie, Soon it will shake you, Gent - ly a - wake you, Then you'll be a pret - ty but - ter -

2.'Doucement', dit le vent,
'Doucement, chenille-enfant',
Couché en cocon tu dors,
Il te secouera,
Pour te reveiller,
Puis tu seras joli papillon.

Life in the rainforest

David Moses

Bright calypso

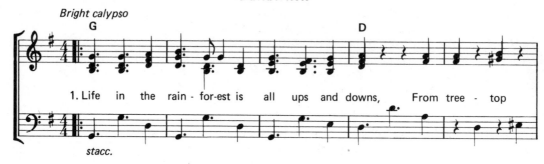

1. Life in the rain - for-est is all ups and downs, From tree - top

stacc.

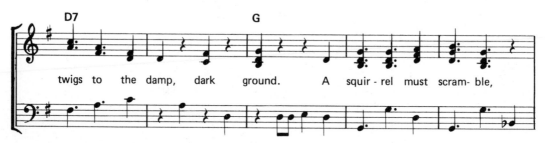

twigs to the damp, dark ground. A squir - rel must scram- ble,

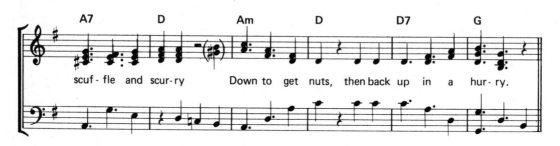

scuf - fle and scur-ry Down to get nuts, then back up in a hur-ry.

Chorus

Squir-rel run, squir-rel climb, Squir-rel fly from tree to tree, There is

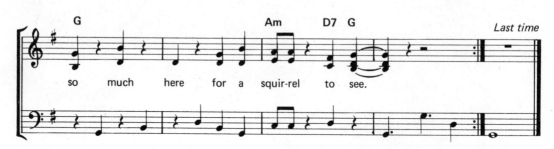

Last time

so much here for a squir-rel to see.

2.Life in the rainforest can be lots of fun.
On high, thin branches beneath the hot sun
The squirrel sees toucans and parrots so bright,
Butterflies dance in the heat and the light.

Chorus

3.Here in the rainforest there's noise all the time,
Monkeys shriek as they leap and climb.
Cawing and screeching, the birds never stop
In branches of trees that are close to the top.

Chorus

4.Squirrels in rainforest should not take a chance,
A leopard might lurk in a low down branch.
There's many a creature thinks squirrels are yummy,
They don't want to end up in somebody's tummy.

Chorus

5.Dark, still and steamy is life on the ground,
Termites and ants in the debris abound.
Okapi and bongo stand still in the heat,
A jungle fowl scratches for something to eat.

Chorus

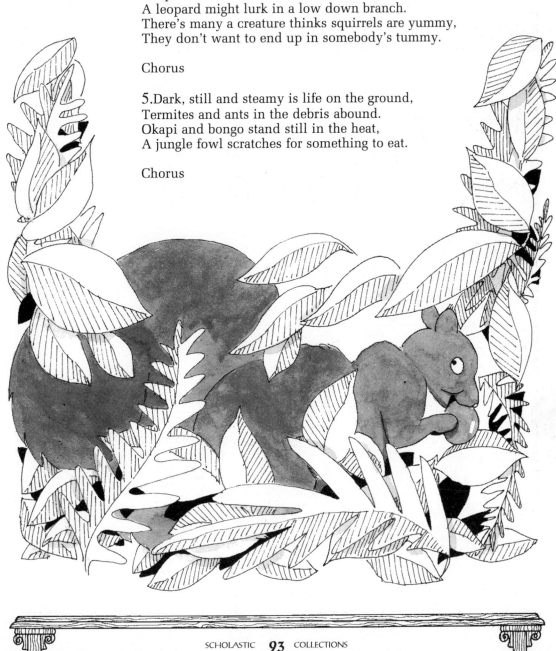

Chop chop

Ann Bryant

(Left hand staccato throughout)

Chop chop! goes the wood - cut-ter, Chop chop! goes the wood - cut-ter,

Chop chop! goes the wood - cut-ter, Swing-ing his axe as he

chops the wood. 1. And the birds in the woods, they

fly a - way at the sound of the chop chop chop! The

birds in the woods they fly a - way at the sound of the chop chop chop!

2. And the mice in the woods they scurry away...
3. And the bunnies in the woods they hop away...
4. And the squirrels in the woods they scamper away...
5. And the wolf in the woods, he creeps away...

The herb song

Chris Williams

2. Among the herbs that grow in my garden,
You'll find Greek parsley and thyme,
Bronze fennel, sorrel and French tarragon.

Chorus

3. Among the herbs that grow in my garden,
You'll find sage, burnet and bay,
Green lovage, borage and lemony balm.

Chorus

See the river run

Clive Barnwell

2.There's a factory
Hiding in the dust,
And the water's changed
From a crystal blue to rust,
And its hard to say
Why the water's used that way.

Chorus

3.There's an animal
Washed up on the bank,
And the water's changed
From a deep red rust to black.
Can't you understand
It's my future in your hand?

Chorus *(repeat the last line twice).*

Pollution is banned

Ian Henderson Begg

Way back in his-t'ry___ when gi-ants did roam The for-ests___ of
Eng-land, it was their home, They cared for the bush-es, ___ the
plants and the trees, Looked af-ter the crea-tures and guid-ed the

Chorus

bees; So don't rouse the gi-ants, Take care of your land, Keep it
clean, Keep it ti-dy, ___ Pol-lu-tion is banned.

2. Way back in hist'ry when giants were 'round,
Man wasn't foolish, he cared for the ground.
He didn't exploit it, he didn't cause strife,
He cared for his homeland that gave him his life.

Chorus

3. Way back in hist'ry when giants had gone,
They handed the country for man to care on.
They took their long rest 'neath the land of their love,
But kept watchful eyes on what happened above.

Chorus

EARTH, AIR, FIRE AND WATER

Peter Morrell

1. Earth, air, fire and water All the in-gre-di-ents of na-tur-al life, Earth, air, fire and wa-ter, They are ba-sic for our plan-et to sur-vive.

2. Earth, air, fire and water,
All there together for our planet to grow.
Earth, air, fire and water,
But is air still pure to breathe, do rivers flow?

Chorus

3. Earth, air, fire and water,
All there to help us as we try to progress.
Earth, air, fire and water,
But don't take them all for granted, show respect.

Chorus

How the world began (a round)

Gillian Parker

The following ostinatos could be played as an introduction and continued through the song.

For recorder:

For tuned percussion:

Voice 1 — 1. This tale was told round camp fires Two

Voice 2 — This tale was told round

thou- sand years a - go. A leg- end tel - ling of a time Be -

camp fires Two thou- sand years a - go. A leg- end tel - ling

- fore the hills or snow. Be - fore the trees, be - fore the plants, Be -

of a time Be - fore the hills or snow. Be - fore the trees, Be -

-fore the world be - gan, A leg- end tel - ling of a land Cre -

- fore the plants, Be - fore the world be - gan, A leg- end tel - ling

    - a - ted   round   a   sun.

    of   a   land   Cre - a - ted   round   a   sun.

2.A legend of a raven
Who flew across the sea
In search of land, in search of rock,
In search of plants and trees.
Who dropped some pebbles from his beak
Into the blue below,
And islands sprung up from the deep
And grass began to grow.

3.The land was green with forests,
The forests filled with herds,
The raven filled the sea with fish,
He filled the sky with birds.
The mountains reached towards the clouds,
The streams gushed from their beds,
The meadows hummed with bumble bees,
The flowers raised their heads.

4.The raven looked about him,
Well pleased with what he saw,
And yet it seemed that something else
Was needed, something more.
He mixed up clay with wood so sweet
And tried and tried, until
A man and woman stood at last –
His world was now complete.

Fire!

Ann Bryant

Steady, rhythmic

1. Flick - er, flick - er, flick - er, flick - er. Smoke is curl - ing thick - er,

fire is grow - ing quick - er And the ti - ni - est flame, ____ licks a

lit - tle bit fur - ther Spread - ing the fire ____ Just a

lit - tle bit more, ____ And the flames climb up high ____ and the

sparks start to fly, ____ And the smoke fills the sky. ____ It's the

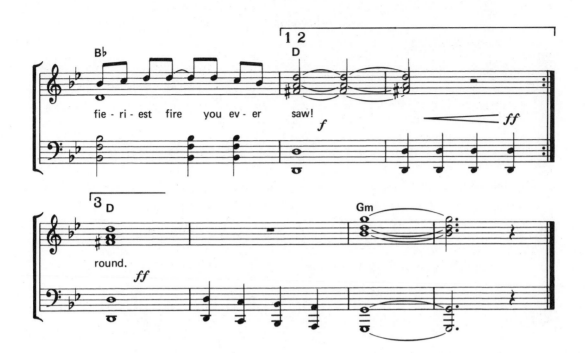

fie - ri - est   fire   you ev - er   saw!   *f*   *ff*

round.   *ff*

2.Nee Nah Nee Nah Nee Nah Nee Nah*
Coming to our aid from the fire brigade
Is the smallest red dot getting bigger and bigger,
Closer and closer, its sirens a-blare.
And the great hoses swoop and the jets loop the loop
And the flames stretch and stoop
There's a fire-water soup in the air!

3.Water, water, water, water,
Wet it, wash it, squirt it, jet it, splosh it, spurt it,
Till the last little flame says goodbye to the world,
Cinders like flakes, soft and black on the ground.
And the sky that was bright, turns to grey what was white,
Turns to dark what was light,
As the shadows of night gather round!

*Imitating fire engine siren

Poles apart

David Moses

1. There's a sea of ice and snow Where pen-guins ne-ver go. There's a land of frost and freeze That a puf-fin ne-ver sees. For the life they lead is poles a-part,— North and south, they're poles a-part,— half a world a-way. - way. Though seve-ral kinds of birds, Seals— which live in herds And wal-rus-es with whis-kers round their mouth, Share the po-lar chill with whales—that live on krill, Some live in the north and some live in the south, Where the ground is fro-zen so hard-ly a-ny-thing will grow. While the north turns out to be just a mass of fro-zen sea, And the ends of the Earth are

poles a - part,___ North and south, they're poles a - part,___

Wind blown, ice - cold poles a - part _ Which are half a world a - way.

2.Polar bears might make a meal
Out of fish or baby seal,
But the ice fish is OK,
It lives twelve thousand miles away.

Chorus

3.Where the Arctic foxes go,
White fur melts against the snow,
But they'll never hunt or roam
Where the penguins have their home.

Chorus

4.Though the narwhal has a horn
Like a fishy unicorn,
It will never feel the freeze
Of Antarctic polar seas.

Chorus

I am the water

Chris Williams

Flowing

I am the wa - ter, I am the sea; I am the waves that turn—

back to the sea; I am the rain - clouds ris - ing high;

I am the snow and hail— that fall from— the sky;

I am the brooks and streams that go tum- bl -ing by;

I am the ri - ver at the est - ua -ry;

I am the wa - ter, I am the sea.

A rippling semiquaver accompaniment such as this works very well:

etc.

Ped.

Desert round

Chris Williams

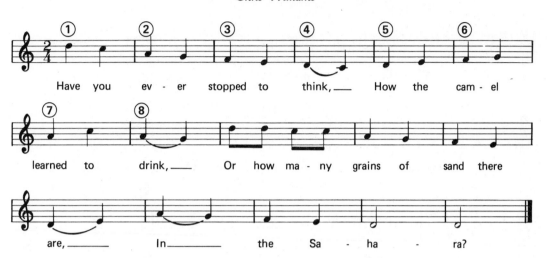

Have you ev - er stopped to think, ___ How the cam - el

learned to drink, ___ Or how ma - ny grains of sand there

are, ___ In ___ the Sa - ha - ra?

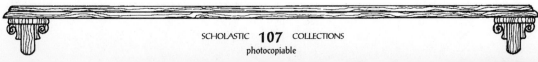

The Weather-or-Nots

Peter Morrell

Chorus

 It's the Wea-ther-or-Nots, the Wea-ther-or-Nots and they're

com - ing out to play. What have the Wea-ther-or-Nots, the

Wea-ther-or-Nots got in store for us to - day?

1. Mon-day's wash day here's the rain, Splash, splash, splash,

Then the light-ning and the thun-der, Crash, crash, crash, C - rash. It's the

Chorus

2. Tuesday starts with hail and snow,
Crunch, crunch, crunch.
Playing snowballs makes us late for
Lunch, lunch, lunch — yum, yum!

Chorus

3. Wednesday's warmer, starts to thaw,
Slush, slush, slush.
Sweep the playground and the paths,
Brush, brush, brush — sweep, sweep!

Chorus

4. Thursday brings a lot of cloud,
Gloom, gloom, gloom.
Getting thicker, now it's foggy,
Boom, boom, boom — boom, boom!

Chorus

5. Friday brightens with the sun,
Great, great, great.
Everyone can now play out,
Wait, wait, wait — who for?

For the Weather-or-Nots
(repeat Chorus from *)

Lots of weather!

Gillian Parker

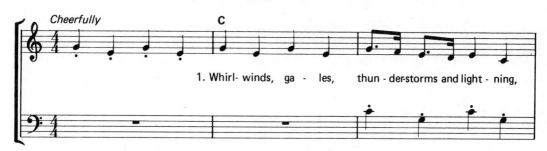

1. Whirl- winds, ga - les, thun - der-storms and light - ning,

Rain - fall, snow - fall, black clouds fill the sky. Hail stones, flash floods,

sun - shine if we're luc - ky. That's the Bri - tish wea - ther In Ju - ly!

2. Foggy, misty, chilly in the mornings.
Icy, freezing, white clouds fill the sky.
Windy, gusty, blowy in the garden.
That's the British weather
In July!

3. Dewy, sunny, gentle summer breezes.
Warm sun, hot sun, no clouds in the sky.
Sad my holiday was over last week.
That's the British weather
In July!

Brrrr!

Gillian Parker

Lyrics beneath the music:

1. Hud-dle in the cor-ner of the play-ground, Shi-ver, shi-ver, chat-ter, chat-ter teeth, Stamp-ing feet, knock-ing knees, Jump-ing up and down in the ic-y breeze. Wish I had my gloves and scarf on, Then I would-n't feel so cold! Brrrr! Freez-ing face,

freez - ing nose, freez - ing fin - gers and freez - ing toes!

2.Whistle blows, we stand still in the playground,
Shiver, shiver, chatter, chatter teeth,
Get in line, file inside,
Shut the classroom door, don't leave it open wide.
Teacher makes me take my coat off,
Shiver in the chilly cloakroom, brrrr!
Freezing face, freezing nose,
Freezing fingers and freezing toes.

3.Nice and warm and cosy in the classroom,
No more shiver, shiver, chatter teeth,
Snow clouds come, fill the skies,
Feeling warm and sleepy, so I shut my eyes,
Fold my arms and lay my head down,
Hide behind my big school bag,
Glowing face, glowing nose,
Glowing fingers and glowing toes.

4.'Who can I hear snoring in my classroom?'
Snore, snore, grunt, grunt, groan.
'It's too warm,' teacher grins –
Opens all the windows, lets the cold air in.
Snow blows in and settles on me –
Makes my face and hands feel cold, sob,
Freezing face, freezing nose,
Freezing fingers and freezing toes.

5.Huddle in the corner of the classroom,
Shiver, shiver, chatter, chatter teeth,
Stamping feet, knocking knees,
Keeping wide awake in the icy breeze,
Wish I had my gloves and scarf on,
Then I wouldn't feel so cold! Brrrr!
Freezing face, freezing nose,
Freezing fingers and freezing toes.

Snow all over the ground

David Moses

(tap knees)
When I woke up this morn-ing and took a look a-round,

(clap clap)
blow me what did I see? Snow all ov-er the ground.

(tap knees)
Snow all ov-er the hous-es, snow all ov-er the trees.

(clap clap)
Cor mate, is-n't it great, al-most up to my knees.

(tap knees)
I put on my coat and scarf, could-n't wait to get out-side.

(clap clap)
Off to the park with Don-na and Mark for a to-bog-gan ride.

little . . . . by . . . . little . . . . . *(tap knees)* . . . . .
Climb-ing up to the top of the hill get-ting slow-er as we climb.

Repeat twice
. . . . gradually . . . . speed . . . . up *(clap clap)*
Fast-er and fast-er down we race, hav-ing a fine old time.

The song of the winter wind

Chris Williams

Oo

Oo

Oo

Fine

1. 'Let me in at your win-dow,' cries the cold win-ter wind, 'Let me
2. 'I have whist-led on ice floes, I have drummed with the hail, I have

tell you the sto-ry of where I have been: Let me tell of the
sung with the snow-goose And hummed with the whale, And I once had my

Arc-tic where I danced with Jack Frost, And of ic-y Si-be-ri-a and
break fast with an old Es-ki-mo We had por-ridge of ic-i-cles and

how I got lost, Oo
toast spread with snow.   'I jumped ov-er the
                                                  Now I'm tired and I'm

ice-bergs and skipped ov-er seas, And I gave ev-ery wal-rus a cough and a
hun-gry, I'm chilled to the bone, All my bold ser-en-ades have died down to a

sneeze, Then I raced with the rein-deer to give San-ta a scare, And I
moan, Let me in at your win-dow, let me sit by your hearth, I'm in

froze off the nose and toes of a wool-ly Po-lar bear! Oo
need of my beau-ty sleep and a ve-ry ve-ry hot bath!

The winter castle

Ann Bryant

Quite fast, menacing

1. No you can't come in here 'cause I'm here, And I'm
drum-ming on the earth and I'm drum-ming on the walls, And I'm
bounc-ing off the win-dows where the fac-es look so pale. Yes I'm
drum-ming ev'-ry-where ___ I'm hail! No you

2.No you can't come in here 'cause I'm here,
And I'm rattling round the house and I'm rattling on the roof,
And I'm laughing at the shutters as they rattle back and forth.
Yes I'm rattling like the wind from the North!

3.No you can't come in here 'cause I'm here,
And I'm splintering the grass and I'm splintering the ground,
And I'm writing on the windows with a crayon like a crack.
Yes I'm splintering like frost — I'm Jack!

4.No you can't come in here 'cause I'm here,
And I'm blanketing the hills and I'm blanketing the trees,
And I've taken all the warmth, that's why the birds have had to go.
Yes I'm blanketing the world — I'm snow!

5.No you can't come in here 'cause I'm here.
I'm more deadly than the snow, I'm more deadly than the frost,
I'm more deadly than the wind and hail, more deadly than a vice.
Nobody can cut through me,
Nobody can cut through me —
I'm ICE!

Rain drops

David Moses

1. Rain drops, rain drops, fall from the sky, Water the plants when the ground gets dry. Rain drops, rain drops, blown by the breeze, Make streams and rivers flow down to the sea.

Chorus
Pattering splattering on the window pane, Running down the gutter and pouring down the drain, Making the grass grow green again. What would we do if there wasn't any rain?

2. Rain drops, rain drops dripping away,
Falling from clouds that are heavy and grey.
Rain drops, rain drops tumble to the ground,
Fill ponds and puddles for us to splash around.

Chorus

3. Rain drops, rain drops, bouncing off the street,
Dribbling down your neck and soaking your feet.
Rain drops, rain drops, glistening in the sun,
Shining like a jewel when the clouds have gone.

Chorus

I'm so hot

David Moses

1. I'm so hot, it's no joke. I could drink a whole can of Coke.

2. I'm so hot, ev-en in the shade. I would love a lit-re of le-mon-ade.

3. I'm so hot, I should think I need a buc-ket of pink fiz-zy drink.

4. I'm so hot, think I ough-ta be ab-le to fin-ish up a bath full of wa-ter.

5. I'm so hot, I could take a swim-ming pool full of van-il-la milk-shake.

6. I'm so hot, I have a no-tion I could swal-low the At-lan-tic Oc-ean.

Shine cold, shine hot

David Moses

capo 3 for guitar chords in brackets

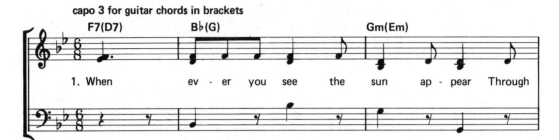

1. When ev - er you see the sun ap - pear Through

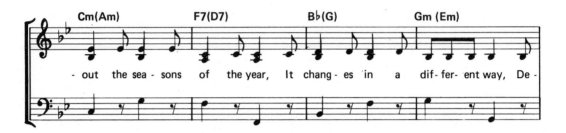

- out the sea - sons of the year, It chang - es in a dif - fer- ent way, De -

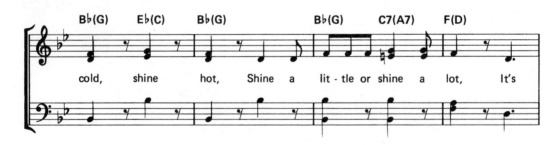

-pend - ing on the wea-ther and the time of day. Shine

Chorus

cold, shine hot, Shine a lit - tle or shine a lot, It's

good to see the sun (clap clap) when-ev - er it comes.

2.At the beginning of the year
The sun is cool, but bright and clear,
Glittering on the frosty ground,
Making branches sparkle as the snow falls down.

Chorus

3.The sun in spring lights up the hills
Like gold and yellow daffodils.
It hides, and then comes out again,
Washed clean and shiny by the April rain.

Chorus

4.The summer sun is hot and high,
Fierce and blazing in the sky,
Radiating light and heat,
Sizzling up the pavement beneath your feet.

Chorus

5.Imagine a misty autumn dawn,
The dew is heavy upon the lawn,
The rising sun is watery white,
And later, huge and orange as it sets at night.

Chorus

Don't let the sunny days go

Clive Barnwell

1. There was once a time peo - ple used to say,
sun be - gan to shine, The ground be - gan to crack, The

That the sun should shine a lot And ne - ver go a -
peo - ple want - ed wa - ter now And wished the rain would

way, But shine on all the day. The back. If the
come a - gain And bring the wa - ter

Leaves are gent - ly fal - ling And a win - ter chill fills the
wind blows ov - er storm clouds And the gar - den's cov - ered in

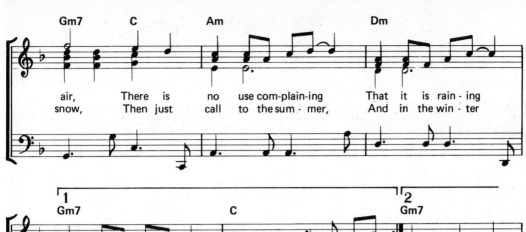

air, There is no use com-plain-ing That it is rain-ing
snow, Then just call to the sum - mer, And in the win - ter

Or that the wea-ther's un - fair. And when the Don't let the

sun - ny days go. Don't let the

sun - ny days go.

2. At last the water came
And flooded all the land,
The green returned to grass and trees,
The calm was broken by the breeze
That brought the rain inland.
But still the rain fell down,
The sky stayed cold and grey,
The people wished the clouds would clear
So they could see the sun again
That shone on through the day.

Chorus *(repeat last line twice)*

Sunshine

Gillian Parker

Ped.....

2.There are places on this earth
Where no plants will grow,
Where the sun beats down each day
On the sand below,
Where the water's turned to mud where
   rivers used to flow,
And the soil is turned to dust as the
   hot winds blow.

3.There are places on this earth
Where the plants all grow,
Where the rain falls every day
And there's never snow,
Where the humming-birds dart through
   the light and shadow,
And the sunshine fills the sky with
   a rainbow.

Brixton market

David Moses

Reggae beat

Introduction and repeat throughout

Chorus

Brix-ton Mar-ket   if you ne-ver been there

I'm gon-na tell   you   What I've seen there: Street   and ar-cade

with shop and stall,   Hus-tle   a-bus-tle   and tra-ders call:

1. Hot   chil-li pep-per!   What you got? I   got   skel-lion and to-ma-tis

What you got? I   got   ripe, jui-cy man-go!   What you got? I   got

green   ba-na-na!   What you got? I   got   fine   fresh   gin-ger root!

What you got? I   got   yam   ve-ry cheap to-day!   O.   K.

2. Sellers
I got fine chad and herring!
I got dried salt fish!
I got mackerel and snapper!
I got best red mullet!
I got no crab meat!
I got prawns and clams

Buyers
What you got?
What you got?
What you got?
What you got?
What you got?
OK.

It's noisy

Gillian Parker

It's noi - sy in the ci - ty, with bu - ses, cars and trains, The

mo - tor bikes go roar - ing by, the sky is filled with planes.

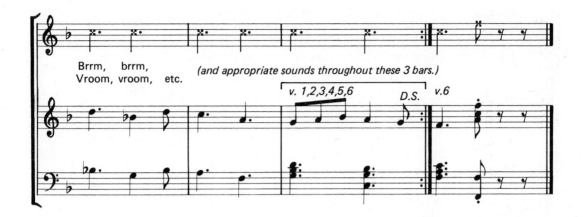

Brrm,   brrm,
Vroom,   vroom,   etc.   *(and appropriate sounds throughout these 3 bars.)*

v. 1,2,3,4,5,6   D.S.   v.6

2.It's noisy in the market,
The people shout and say,
'Bananas, apples, fruit and veg,
All going cheap today!'   *(Bananas, apples, pears, etc.)*

3.It's noisy in the country,
The birds sing in the trees,
The flowers nod their heads and hum
With busy bumble bees.   *(Tweet, chirrup, hum, buzz, etc.)*

4.It's noisy at the seaside,
The gulls shriek in the sky,
The waves thud on the sandy beach,
The children shout and cry.   *(Screech, shh-shh, yippee, etc.)*

5.It's noisy when it's stormy
With thunder, hail and rain,
The wind howls round the chimney pots
And bangs the doors again.   *(Howl, whoosh, bang, etc.)*

6.I'm noisy when I'm happy,
I'm noisy every day.
I jump and sing and stamp and clap
And shout, 'HIP, HIP, HOORAY!'

Sounds (a round)

Gillian Parker

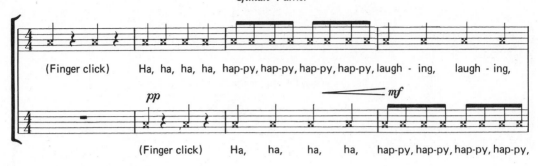

(Finger click) Ha, ha, ha, ha, hap-py, hap-py, hap-py, hap-py, laugh - ing, laugh - ing,

pp   *mf*

(Finger click) Ha, ha, ha, ha, hap-py, hap-py, hap-py, hap-py,

ha, ha, ha, ha, ha, ha, ha, ha, HA! HA! mak-ing lots of high sounds,

sf   *sf*

laugh - ing, laugh - ing, ha, ha, ha, ha, ha, ha, ha, ha, HA! HA!

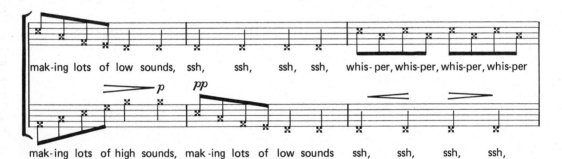

mak-ing lots of low sounds, ssh, ssh, ssh, ssh, whis-per, whis-per, whis-per, whis-per

p   *pp*

mak-ing lots of high sounds, mak-ing lots of low sounds ssh, ssh, ssh, ssh,

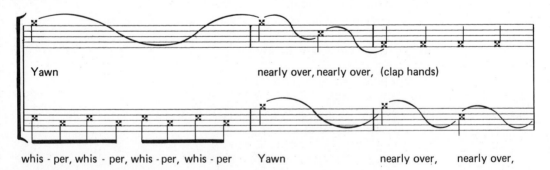

Yawn   nearly over, nearly over, (clap hands)

whis - per, whis - per, whis - per, whis - per Yawn nearly over, nearly over,

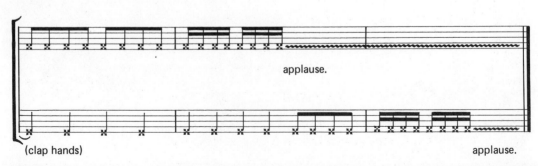

applause.

(clap hands)   applause.

HOW DID WE TRAVEL?

Gillian Parker

How did we tra-vel in the old-en _____ days, On a

horse, in a coach, in a trap? In a bas-si-nette or pram, on a

trol-ley-bus or tram? Did we get there with a com-pass or a map?__

2. How did your Grandad make his way to work?
Did he walk, did he drive, did he ride
On a penny-farthing bike, on a tandem, or a trike,
Or an Austin with a hooter on the side?

3. How did your Mum get in to town today?
In a Honda with her chauffeur, Dennis Russ?
In her chopper, in her plane, or by taxi or by train,
Or did Uncle Alan drive her in his bus?

4. How did you make your way to school today?
Did you stroll, did you run, did you hop?
Did you dawdle, did you hide, did you leapfrog, did you slide?
'No, I stopped and bought a lolly at the shop!'

photocopiable

Getting around

Debbie Campbell

1. Did — you know that long a - go they said — the world was

flat and so, They did - n't dare to go too near the side?

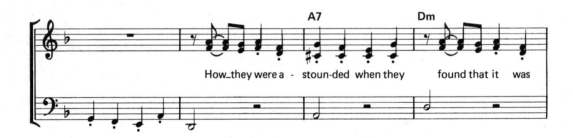

How — they were a - stoun-ded when they found that it was

roun-ded. Now they tra - vel all a - round it far and wide.

Now - a - days we've ma - ny — ways to go from A to

2. People say that everyday they find another kind of way
To travel even faster than before.
Could it be that very soon we'll all be going to the moon?
I wonder what the future has in store.

Hover in a helicopter high above the town,
Travel in a tunnel going underneath the ground,
Fly up in the sky aboard a plane,
Ride around the countryside by train.
Ride around the countryside by train.

Foot work

Gillian Parker

I start-ed with a

tri - cy - cle, Then wob-bled on a bi - cy - cle.

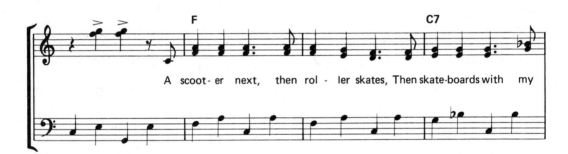

A scoot-er next, then rol - ler skates, Then skate-boards with my

bro-ther's mates. ___ A B - M - X for

Christ-mas and a rac - er for my birth - day. ___

How did we travel?

Then a mo-tor bike with lea-thers To pro-tect me in all

wea - thers._____ And when

Revving up noise

I have passed my dri - ving test, I'll buy a car

All sounds together!!

and have a rest!

Travelling man

Debbie Campbell

1. I know a man who

knew a man who flew to the sun in a fry-ing-pan.

It got too hot and he could-n't set-tle, So he

flew back home in a whist-ling ket-tle.

It's a sil-ly song and you can sing a-long,

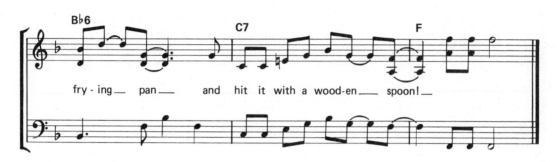

> Bang to the rhy-thm of the tune. Get a ket - tle or a
> fry - ing __ pan __ and hit it with a wood-en __ spoon! __

2.I know a man who knew a man who
Flew to the moon in a watering can.
It got too cold living in a crater,
So he flew back home in a cheese grater.

Chorus

Motor car

David Moses

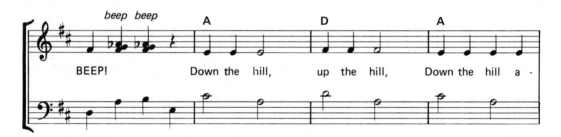

2. Motor car, motor car,
Climb the hill so steep, BEEP! BEEP!
Motor car, motor car,
Climb the hill so steep, BEEP! BEEP!
Down the hill, up the hill,
Down and up you go.
You can stop when you reach the top, going very slow.

3. Motor car, motor car,
Down the other side at last, BEEP! BEEP!
Motor car, motor car,
Down the other side at last, BEEP! BEEP!
Down the hill, up the hill,
Down now all the way.
Faster and faster off we go along the motorway.

Traffic song

Debbie Campbell

Have you seen Stan in a mail van, hur-ry-ing, rac-ing round the town, chas-ing up and down? Have you seen Stan in a mail van, hur-ry-ing, rac-ing round and round the town?

Chorus

Rid-ing a-long he/she whis-tles a song, trav el-ling on his/her way. Peo-ple all shout when Stan is a-bout, Bet-ter stay out the way.

Make up your own verses for this song, e.g. Joyce in a Rolls-Royce,
Mike on a push bike, Gus on a red bus, etc.

Travel by water

Gillian Parker

1. I am punt - ing, gen-tly punt - ing on a sum - mer's af - ter - noon, Past the dream - ing spires of Ox-ford, past the mea - dows in full bloom. _

2. I am drifting through the warm canals of Venice in July,
I see gondolas, the Bridge of Sighs, St Mark's, where pigeons fly.

3. I am sailing, gently sailing in a breeze along the Nile,
Past the Pyramids and camels, past the Sphinx's secret smile.

4. I am chugging, slowly chugging up the Mississippi River,
On an ancient paddle-steamer, filled with letters to deliver.

5. I am rushing, quickly rushing through the rapids by canoe,
Over whirlpools, over rocks towards the river far below.

6. I am spinning, twisting, turning in a barrel, holding tight,
As I plunge down through Niagara Falls, through rainbows dancing bright.

7. I am dancing, ducking, flying on my surfboard on the sea,
Over rollers, over breakers, it's the Bondi Beach for me.

8. There are many ways to travel over water, if you wish –
You could, of course, jump in and swim, like any common fish!

NB: This is a pentatonic tune and can be played by tuned percussion using the notes C,D,F,G,A or (without the piano accompaniment) on the black notes of a keyboard.

The chug-chug song

Peter Morrell

1. Meet the Cap-tain Tea-pot Lid   and his   wife called   Flo,

mf

Bar-gees all their lives,   trav'-lling to   and   fro,   Bir-ming-ham to

War - wick, ___   Coal to town his - to - ric, ___   Sing-ing as they

chug be - neath the   brid-ges oh so   low. ___   It's the

f

op - en air and free-dom that we   love. ___   It's the

f

2. Teapot Lid's worked all his life on a barge called Meg,
Through the many locks and the tunnels to leg,
Old day horses towing,
Now the engine's flowing,
Hands upon the tiller and a cosy on his head.

Chorus

3. There are roses, lakes and castles on the cabin door,
Painted pots and pans, wooden spoons galore,
Panels coloured brightly,
Ropes coiled up so tightly.
Everything looks ship-shape as the crew complete their chores.

Chorus

4. Passing chimneys, passing wharfs, as they move the coal,
Butties strung behind make a heavy load,
Down the Hatton Flight,
Warwick's now in sight,
Soon the coal will burn and bring its warmth to many a soul.

Chorus

Summer on the river

Chris Williams

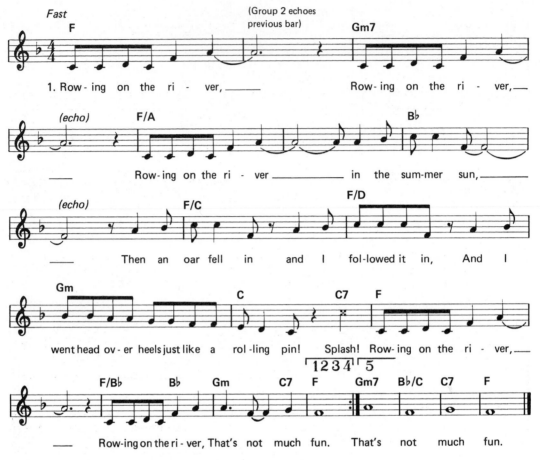

(An alternative version is to take each verse a semitone higher, so that verse 5 is in A major.)

2. Punting on the river *(repeat)*,
Punting on the river in the summer sun.
It was just my luck that the pole got stuck
And I dived into the water like a rubber duck – quack!
Punting on the river *(repeat)*,
That's not much fun.

3. Sailing on the river *(repeat)*,
Sailing on the river in the summer sun.
Then I hit the bank and the dinghy sank
And I went right overboard as if I'd walked the plank – splash!
Sailing on the river *(repeat)*,
That's not much fun.

4. Fishing by the river *(repeat)*,
Fishing by the river in the summer sun.
Then I caught a trout and it splashed about
And it pulled me in the river in a wrestling bout – glug!
Fishing by the river *(repeat)*,
That's not much fun.

Flying high

Peter Morrell

Gently

D   **C**   **D**   **C**

mp Oh I wish I could fly like a bird in the sky, Or a
I could go where I please ov-er build-ings and trees, It's so

D   **C**   **D**   **C etc,**

glid-er with wings of a gull. Through the cen-tur-ies Man longed to
ea-sy and life's ne-ver dull. But what's hap-pen-ing now? I feel

1

have a wing span that would lift his feet high off the ground.
diff'-rent some how. We have lift off and I'm sky-ward

2

With freedom

D7   Chorus   **G**   **Am**

bound. Now I'm fly-ing a-long,— It seems no-thing is wrong— and the

f

D7   **G**   **C**   **D7**   **G**

song that I sing's 'Fly-ing High.'— I can ho-ver and swoop, There I've

Am   **F**   **D7**   **G**

just looped the loop.— Now I'm off round the world— fly-ing high.

The magic tree

Leonora Davies

Chorus

There are ap - ple trees and man - go trees, There are

prick - ly trees and pret - ty ones, But my fav-ourite tree is The

Ma - gic Tree and it's down at the bot - tom in the

cor - ner by the fence of Mis - ter No - bo-dy's gar - den. *Fine*

1. When I climb up high__ I can see,__ For - ev - er and a

Chorus

2. There's a secret door inside the trunk
Which opens up for me.
When I step inside I wish a wish –
Shall I travel to the moon and back today?
Oh yes!

Chorus

The land that time forgot

Clive Barnwell

1. I would like to sail ov-er all the seas, With the sun-shine on my back and sails filled with the breeze, And I would search al-most a-ny-where and spend all I had got, As I went on my quest to find The land that time for - got.

2. - got. Where di - no-saurs eat leaves from an - cient trees And
Where an - cient birds look just like great big bats And

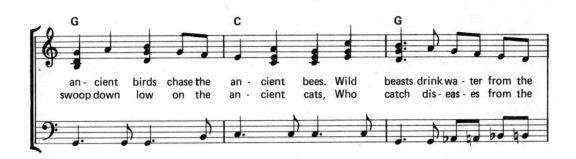

Second time   D.C. al fine

Lyrics under the music:

an - cient birds chase the an - cient bees. Wild beasts drink wa - ter from the
swoop down low on the an - cient cats, Who catch dis - eas - es from the

an - cient seas In the land that time for - got.
an - cient rats In the land that time for - got.

2. I would sail through rain I would sail through snow,
I would sail to north and south and everywhere I'd go,
And I would discard the weather be it cold, wet or hot,
As I went on my quest to find
The land that time forgot.

Chorus

3. Maybe I will find what I seek one day,
Somewhere that is very close or many miles away,
But until then I'll keep searching and as likely as not
I will search all my life to find
The land that time forgot.

Into orbit

Gillian Parker

Count down 10, 9, 8, 7, 6, 5, 4, 3, 2, 1, ze - ro Blast off!

1. I'm rush-ing in my roc-ket, zoom-ing up-wards, climb-ing high Through the

at - mos-phere and stra - tos- phere, as as - ter -oids fly by, Way a -

- bove the world, a- bove the clouds, a - bove the bright blue sky, To the

mys-ter-ies of out -er space, be-yond the hu -man eye. 2. To a -

hur - ry home for tea.

Mis - sion ov - er, out.

2.To another world where no one's ever heard of motor cars,
To another world of black holes, UFOs and meteors,
Through a storm of cosmic dust and ash, a galaxy of stars,
As I hurtle through the light-years on my way to visit Mars.

3.Then from Mars to Jupiter, and on to my next destination,
Passing through the rings of Saturn to the Uranus Space Station,
Fly to Neptune, fly to Pluto, do a full solar rotation,
End with Mercury and Venus for the Space Confederation.

4.When my mission is completed, all the tests done properly,
All the data is computed, all is satisfactory,
Then I plunge down through the atmosphere and land far out at sea
And I climb out of my capsule and I hurry home for tea.

Mission over,
Out.

Rocket to the stars, rocket to the moon

David Moses

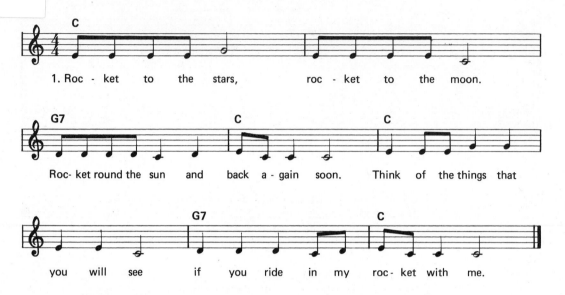

This game requires enough space for the children taking part to divide into three equal groups, each group stationed at the point of a marked or imaginary triangle. The groups are called Sun, Moon and Stars respectively.

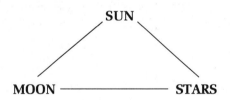

One child, chosen as the rocket pilot, moves around like a rocket between the three groups while the others sing verse one. When the verse is finished the 'pilot' chooses a child (e.g. Sarah) from the nearest group. Sarah now becomes the pilot while the first child joins on behind, and both travel between the groups during verse two.

2.Sarah see the stars, Sarah see the moon,
Sarah see the sun, come back again soon.
Think of the things that you will see
If you ride in my rocket with me.

Each time the singing stops, a new pilot is chosen. Each new pilot could choose an object he or she might see on the space journey; all those on board the rocket have to move round in a manner which suggests the chosen object, e.g. a spinning saucer, a space spider-monster, a shooting star, etc.

Black hole

David Moses

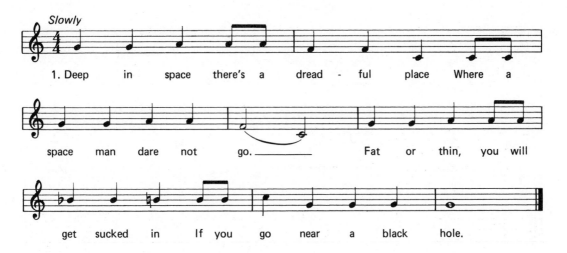

Slowly

1. Deep in space there's a dread - ful place Where a
space man dare not go. _____ Fat or thin, you will
get sucked in If you go near a black hole.

2.Swirling around without a sound,
A whirlpool made of nothing;
It's dark and hollow, whatever it swallows,
It just can't suck enough in.

3.Once you begin to get drawn in,
You can try to alter course;
But do what may, you will not get away
From the black hole's awesome force.

Send a message

Gillian Parker

mes - sage, hope it gets there in one piece.

Ostinato

May be clapped throughout or played on a single note to imitate Morse code. A chime bar or glockenspiel would be most effective.

Chorus

2. Send a message on the drums, send a salute on the guns,
Send a pigeon, send a message in Morse code.
Hoist the flags up on a boat, send a letter, send a note,
Use the post-box at the corner of the road.

Chorus

3. See the lighthouse wink its light to the ships out in the night,
DANGER! DANGER! ROCKS BELOW! its silent warning.
But if you're too late and sink, and you end up in the 'drink',
Send a message in a bottle in the morning.

Chorus

4. Send a message with two cans, or your mother's pots and pans,
But make sure that they are empty when you shout.
Join them with a length of string (garden twine is just the thing),
Pull the line taut, 'Testing, testing, Roger, out.'

Technology grind

Ann Bryant

Fast and frantic

1. Or - ga - ni - sa - tion, — the first big es - sen - tial, — Of - fice e - quip - ment, — the best you can find. — En - ter com - mu - ters, — work on com - pu - ters, — Day af - ter day — the — tech - no - lo - gy grind. — But

Slower and calmer

I pre - fer to work in my gar - den, — To

work in my gar - den__ at home. I have all that I need__ right

here in my gar - den.__ I'm liv - ing the life__ that__ I've grown.____

2.Order the software and order the hardware,
Paper and printout the best of its kind,
Enter commuters, work on computers,
Day after day the technology grind.

Chorus

3.*Tel-i-comm-un-i-ca-phon-i-ca-dict-o
*Dat-a-per-dig-i-tal-au-to-re-wind!
Enter commuters, work on computers
Day after day the technology grind.

* These two lines are supposed to hover between real technology words
and extremely silly made-up 21st century jargon!

Age of the chip

Peter Morrell

1. We're in the twen-ti-eth cen-tu-ry ___ We're in-to high tech-no-lo-gy ___ We're in the age of the train ___ and the boat and the plane, ___ there's a nuc-le-ar ship ___ and the si-li-con chip ___ Yes it's the Age of the Chip ___

2. There's Clare and Paul and then there's Jason too,
These modern children with so much to do,
Now they can visit the moon,
But they come back too soon
From their Universe trip,
Thanks to the silicon chip,
Yes, it's the Age of the Chip.

3. There's *   and Discomania –
The amp's so loud you get a painful ear,
Remote control video,
The real high-tech laser show.
Where it's cool and hip
And they eat microchips,
Yes, it's the Age of the Chip (repeat twice)
And that's it! YEH!

* Children choose a three-syllable pop star/group.

It's our job (The media song)

Ian Henderson Begg

Chorus

It's our job, To find the news, To spread the word A - round the world. 1. The

news— pa - pers take the news In print both far and near. They

tell the truth we like to think, But truth is ne - ver clear. Re -

- mem - ber, we've a job to do. We have to earn our pay. We

print the stor - ies that you read In pa - pers ev - 'ry day.

Chorus

2. The radio it spreads the news,
In sound both far and near.
It tells the truth we like to think
But truth is never clear.
Remember we've a job to do,
We have to earn our pay,
We try to tell the world the truth,
In broadcasts every day.

Chorus

3. The television beams the news
To countries far and near,
It tells the truth we like to think
In pictures very clear.
Remember we've a job to do,
We have to earn our pay,
So switch the box on when you can,
The news is new each day.

LOOKING BACK, LOOKING FORWARD

Peter Morrell

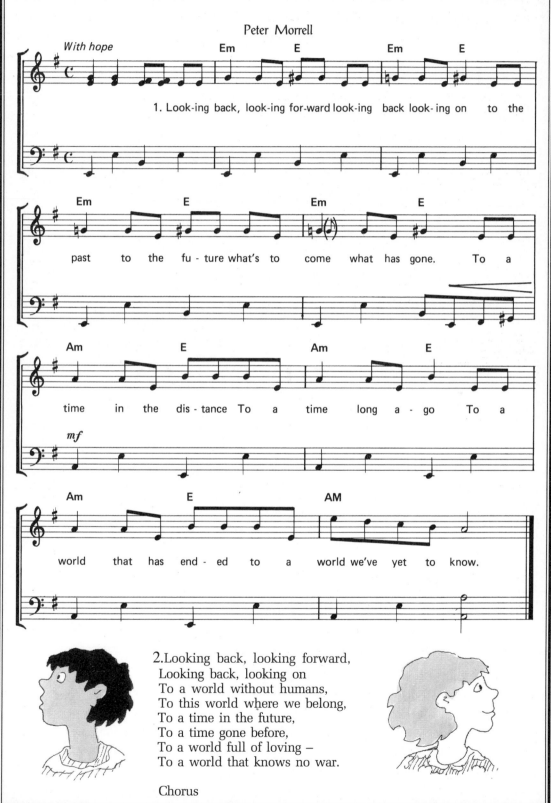

1. Look-ing back, look-ing for-ward look-ing back look-ing on to the past to the fu-ture what's to come what has gone. To a time in the dis-tance To a time long a-go To a world that has end-ed to a world we've yet to know.

2. Looking back, looking forward,
Looking back, looking on
To a world without humans,
To this world where we belong,
To a time in the future,
To a time gone before,
To a world full of loving –
To a world that knows no war.

Chorus

Way up high

Peter Morrell

1. In the days of dis - tant past, When man first looked up from Earth,
Dust and gas cre - ate new life, Heat and light be - come in - tense,

Stared in awe at specks of light, Won-dered how they'd come to life.
Stars are born in dis - tant space, Mys - te - ry of

time and — place, of time and place. Take a look way up high, — See the

stars in the sky, — They're the un - i - ver - se's an - swer — To the

won - ders of the world. Take a won - ders of the world.

It's a monster ... isn't it?

David Moses

1. What sharp claws, what ter - ri - ble, scrat - chy

claws; It's ea - sy to see it could tear up a tree. It could

knock down a house, but it could-n't hurt me . . . Could it?

2. What great jaws, what horrible, slobbery jaws,
Without any fuss, it could swallow a bus,
It could gobble a truck, but it wouldn't hurt us.
Would it?

3. What huge eyes, I've never seen so many eyes,
They flash with colours of very hue,
It can see in the dark, but it can't see you.
Can it?

4. What loud roars, what hollering, howling roars,
They're loud as a train or a big jet plane,
It would frighten a giant, but it wouldn't scare me.
Would it?

The big beasts' boogie

Leonora Davies

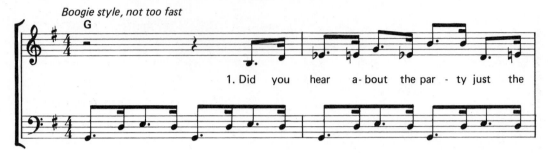

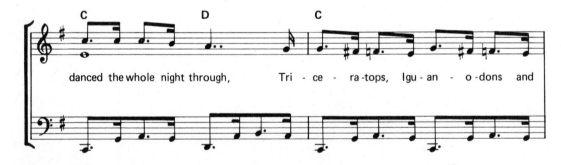

par - ty. _____ Come and hear the din - o-saur - us

band. There are car - ni-vores and her - bi-vores and

lots of oth - er great big jaws, Danc - ing here up-on the ___ sand.

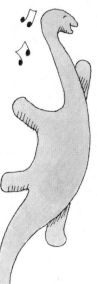

2. There was Stegosaurus jiving, oh beware his spikes,
But the Brontosaurus he just sat down.
Though they stayed there in the water,
   where they swayed the whole night through,
Ichthyosaurus, Plesiosaurus joined the party too.

Chorus

3. The Pteranodons they glided up above their friends,
Every now and then they ate some fish.
Hypsilophodons, Iguanodons, their dancing was so neat,
Great big bodies, legs so short and tiny little feet.

Chorus

4. Though he did look rather savage with his three big horns,
Triceratops he waved his tail
When the king of all the dinosaurs, Tyrannosaurus Rex
Joined the party, goodness me, what's going to happen next!

Chorus

Ballad of Moses

Peter Morrell

1. Now Phar-oah said, 'All
   Phar-oah's daugh-ter

boys must die, Ev-'ry new born son of ev-'ry Is - rae - lite.'
found him there And she showed com - pas -sion and a lov - ing care.

(Is - rae - lite) But Mo - ses' mum thought o - ther - wise, Put
(lov - ing care) 'Go find a He - brew mo - ther now Who'll

Mo - ses in a bas-ket on the Ri - ver Nile. (Ri - ver Nile) Soon
nurse him and look af - ter him as she knows how.'

A little slower
Chorus
Ca - naan is the land of milk and ho - ney,

Ca - naan is where we all be - long. Mo - ses, will you take us all there one day? Mo - ses, we'll be strong, With you we can't go wrong. you we can't go wrong.

2. As Moses watched his sheep one day,
From a burning bush the voice of God did say *(God did say)*,
'I need you as my right hand man
To lead my chosen people to the Promised Land *(Promised Land)*'
But Pharaoh said, 'You cannot go',
So God sent him plagues of frogs and tales of woe *(tales of woe)*,
Like flies and lice and locusts too
Till Pharaoh said, 'Be gone, I've had enough of you.'

Chorus

3. Then later Pharaoh changed his mind
And caught up with Moses and the Israelites *(Israelites)*
Who crossed the Red Sea just ahead
Of Pharaoh and his army who were left for dead *(left for dead)*.
One day God said, 'Don't be afraid,
Here are Ten Commandments which should be obeyed' *(be obeyed)*,
And from that day things went as planned
For soon God's people settled in the Promised Land.

Chorus

A man coming through

Gerald Haigh

Rock blues — lively

1. The cei - ling's fal - ling,_ The plas - ter's com - ing down. (ad lib.)

Noise and com - mo - tion_ And pan - ic all a - round 'Cos there's a

hole ap - pear - ing_ A lit - tle patch of blue. Sud - den - ly there's day - light And

fresh air blow - ing through. There's a man com - ing through the_ roof_

_ My good - ness *(spoken)* Some - one on a stretch - er drop - ping

Use thirds in the right hand for that 'funky feel'!

2. There's faces peering,
And ropes hanging down,
People are staring
Up with a frown.
And then the stretcher lands among us
And there so still
The poor chap on it
Looks pretty ill.

Chorus

3. The Master sees him
And holds his hand,
'Your legs are mended
Now try to stand.'
And then the fellow starts walking
And shouts to tell,
'Thank you Jesus
For making me well'.

Chorus

NB: St Luke tells of a man, sick with the palsy, who was brought by his friends to see Jesus. Because of the crowds, they were unable to get near, and in desperation they went on the roof of the house where Jesus was talking, made a hole and lowered their friend through.

Saints live on!

Peter Morrell

Chorus

Saints live on, of course they do— Don't think that they are dead, Their deeds and words are all a - round In good books to be read. So as we live our dai - ly lives — Let's try to love and care, And then we'll live our own lives As the saints — tried to live theirs.

1. Pa - tience is a vir - tue or at least that's what we're told, Dam - sels wait - ed pa - tient - ly for res - cue by knights bold. And to - day it's just as true as in those days of

old, Lis-ten ve-ry care-ful-ly, a sto-ry to be-hold. _____

2. Number two, endurance, means we've got
  to stick at things,
Don't give up or panic if things don't go
  with a swing.
Just remember somebody who gave up
  ev'rything,
Father Damien helped the lepers, didn't
  stop to think.

Chorus

3. Have you ever said to someone, 'Hey, listen
  to me,
What I say is right and what is more you
  must agree.'
With a bit more tolerance they'll listen
  just you see,
Gandhi searched through life to find
  religious liberty.

Chorus

4. Saints we often think of having lived so
  long ago,
Yet today we see them on TV or video.
One man looked to Africa and said, 'There
  I must go',
Lives he tried to mend and great
  compassion did he show.

Chorus

5. Now our saintly virtues are complete
  except for one,
'Wisdom can be quite a problem', said
  King Solomon,
In our time the wise ones try to see what
  can be done
So our world will live in peace and
  trust in ev'ryone.

Chorus

Be my valentine

Music by Peter Morrell and words by Elizabeth Chapman

searched thro'__ the whole world__ I searched ev - 'ry where For some - one __ to love me__ For some-one to care. I thought I__ had found you,__ I thought you were mine, I wrote you a let - ter__ Be my val - en - tine.

Chorus Don't leave me,__ don't grieve me __ Oh al - ways__ be mine. Don't scorn me,__ for - lorn me,__ I'm your_____ val - en - tine.

2. You tore up the paper,
You threw it away.
You laughed at my feelings,
Oh what could I say?
I gave you a flower,
The best I could find.
I begged and I pleaded
Be my valentine.

Chorus

3. Oh I would fight dragons,
I could be so brave,
Or I would cross oceans
Your life I would save.
If only you'd love me,
If you would be mine,
Once more I must ask you,
Be my valentine.

Chorus

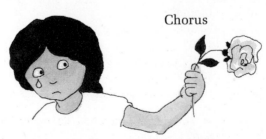

Hay time

Ian Henderson Begg

1. At dawn we must rise when the wea-ther is fair, All
folks come to lend a hand. The vil-lage is there
giv-ing their share, As we all have a share in the land.

Chorus
When it's hay time, come the mid-dle of June, The
sun is high ov-er head. All day we'll mow and
turn the hay, Till we stag-ger home late to bed.

2. It's hard and it's long, but the work must go on,
Once cut it must not lay and rot,
So the women will fork, will rake and then pook*
While the men mow and gather the lot.

Chorus

3. And all the day long the work must go on,
The carts loaded high plodding round
From field to farm, to rick or to barn
Till the year's hay is stacked safe and sound.

Chorus

4. As dusk's shadows fall, it's time for us all
To gather and wander on home,
We villagers all will answer the call
For at harvest we all work as one.

*Pook – to pile hay in small stacks ready for collection by
the horse-drawn carts.

The conker song

Peter Morrell

I came to con - quer and make your throne my own.

and make your throne my, and make your throne my own.

2.**W**: Stand and fight like a man not a mouse,
Don't go running back to your house.
My army's strong with arrows and bows
Horse chestnut trees made those (Dear Harold).

H: But let's play a game of conkers.
W: You must be bonkers,
I've not come all this way to play
A game of conkers.
I came to conquer
And make your throne my own.

3.**H**: Let our armies decide who should win,
I can't stand such a milit'ry din,
A game of conkers is better, oh my,
Than arrows in the eye (Dear William).

W: Then I'll join you in a game of conkers –
They must be bonkers
To come so far and then not play
A game of conkers.
There's time to conquer
And make your throne my
And make your throne my
And make your throne my own.

W: William the Conqueror
H: King Harold

Robin Hood

Clive Barnwell

Fairly quickly

1. Back at the end of the
John was un-pop-u-lar,

twelfth cen-tu-ry, King Ri-chard the Li-on-heart ruled this coun-
gree-dy some say. He taxed peo-ple high-ly, they just could-n't

-try. But fight-ing cru-sades he more of-ten was gone so he
pay. And then a new he-ro ar-rived on the scene and he

left it in the hands of Bro-ther John.
fought for good and dressed in Lin-coln green.

Chorus

Friend of some and foe of more, En-e-my of King John's law,
Home was in the op-en air, Out in Sher-wood For-est, where

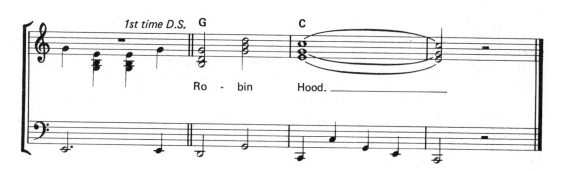

2. Soon there were others who joined him to fight
Against all the things they believed were not right,
King John was aware that a danger had grown
And the trees of Sherwood Forest was its home.

Though he tried hard he could not do a thing
To catch those who thwarted the plans of the King —
He never succeeded. The trees have all gone
But the legend told of Robin Hood lives on.

Chorus

Leonardo

Gerald Haigh

2.Charcoal drawings,
Miracle thoughts working in your mind,
Rising, reaching,
Where were you trying to go,
Leonardo?

3.Secret writing,
Seeking to tell what was in your mind,
Speaking wisdom,
What do you want us to learn,
Leonardo?

4.Vision splendid,
Opening doors on your sunlit mind,
Teaching beauty,
How can we share in your dreams,
Leonardo?

'He devoted his restlessly curious mind and indefatigable
mental energy to a variety of theoretical and practical.
problems... The nineteen known sketchbooks and notebooks
of Leonardo's work reveal his wide range of interests...' *(Oxford
Reference Dictionary).*

Walter Raleigh blues

Peter Morrell

A maritime blues

(That) Take off your coat (Wal- ter) Lay it ov- er that

pool of wa - ter___ Take off your coat and a-

- void the Wal - ter Ra - leigh blues. ___

1. I's just got back from the States_Ma'am

I hope I's not too-oo late_Ma'am I's brought you a

W.R. Walter Raleigh

Q.E.1 Queen Elizabeth 1

2.WR Try this, it's a leaf of tobacco,
Take a sniff, it's got a really big KO.
Best of all is when you rub it up small,
Then put it in your mouth and KAPOW! what a taste.

QE1 I don't wish to know it, put it in your pipe and smoke it.

WR What a good idea, I hadn't thought about doing that.

Famous names

Gillian Parker

1. A sol-dier called Na-po-le-on Led

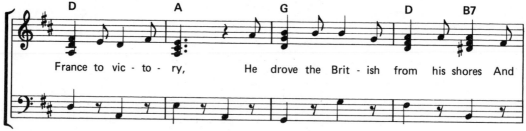

France to vic-to-ry, He drove the Brit-ish from his shores And

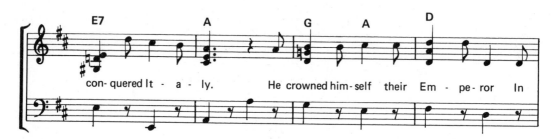

con-quered It - a - ly. He crowned him-self their Em-pe-ror In

eigh - teen hun-dred and four, But lost the Bat-tle of

Wa - ter - loo, Then ruled in France no more.

2.Elizabeth, our 'Good Queen Bess',
Ruled in the 'Golden Age'.
Her sailors plundered Spanish ships
Much to King Philip's rage.
He sent his great Armada out
To halt her glorious reign,
But Drake said, 'Men, we'll sink their boats,
But first let's end our game.'

3.An Englishman called Guy Fawkes
And seven other men
Made plans to blow up Parliament
And murder England's King.
They filled the vaults with gunpowder
To execute their crime.
As Guy Fawkes went to light the fuse
The guards caught him in time.

4.A nurse called Florence Nightingale
In eighteen fifty-four,
Went off to help the wounded men
In the Crimean War.
She worked all day, she worked all night,
In cold and dark and damp,
But always had a kindly word,
This 'Lady with the Lamp'.

My tune has a magic murmur (Pied Piper)

Ann Bryant

Real tennis rag

Music by Peter Morrell and words by Elizabeth Chapman

1. When you want to solve a prob - lem Just go down to the court. _____ Yes, when life is on the down - hill, You've got beau - coup to sort. _____ When you're wav - ing a rac - ket And you're

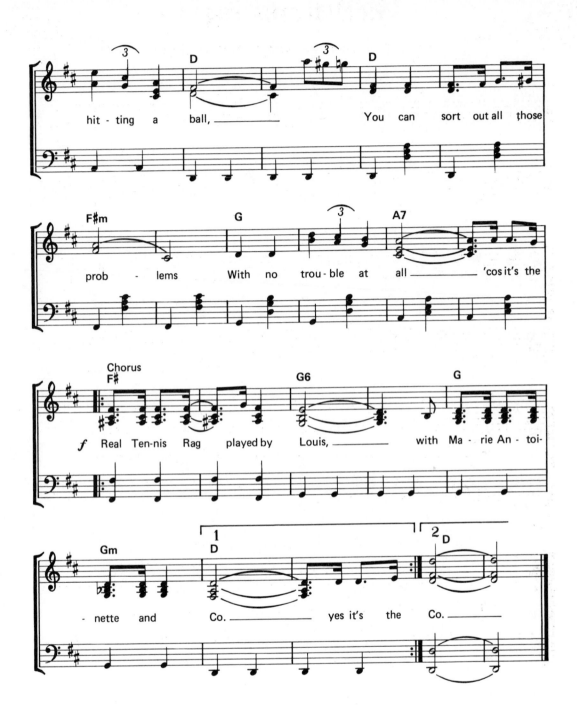

hit - ting a ball, _____ You can sort out all those

prob - lems With no trou - ble at all _____ 'cos it's the

Chorus

f Real Ten-nis Rag played by Louis, _____ with Ma - rie An - toi-

- nette and Co. _____ yes it's the Co. _____

2. When the world seems all against you
And your friends disappear,
When you've blown your final million
And you've hooked all the gear,
Then just hit out a winner,
Blow the lot off the court,
It will make you feel real good man,
Well you know that it ought, 'cos it's the...

Chorus

3. If you lose just shrug your shoulders,
It is all in the game,
Win or lose if rich or poor man,
Life will go on the same.
So just pick up your racket,
Give the game all you've got,
Here today and gone tomorrow,
Life's a game soon forgot, 'cos it's the...

Chorus

We'll all reach out

Clive Barnwell

2. Though I'll never hear your cries,
I'll never feel the pain
That grows inside to hurt you,
I will always be your friend
And in your time of need
You know I won't desert you.

In your land of hunger,
In your land of drought,
Gone are the days,
Gone are the nights,
When people lived
On the earth's delights

Chorus

Send our love around the world

Peter Morrell

Take a pocketful of prayers

Leonora Davies

Chorus

Take a poc-ket-ful of prayers. And a hand-ful of hope. Let's all wish that man will think and pause _____ Take a tray-ful of tears In a world full of woe. Will sense pre-vail and rea-son ov-er rule? _____ Let's pray for peace. _____

1. March-ing men _ with swords a gleam - ing. Row on row _ of stan - dards stream - ing. His - to - ry _ has al - ways told this tale _____ Power and strength the word's a - gres - sion Fear and want _ the word's sub-mis - sion His - to - ry _ will al - ways bear the scars _____ of man's mis - takes. _____

Chorus

2. Mighty guns and tanks a-thundering,
Row on row of men lie bleeding,
History has always told this tale.
Towns and cities lie in ruins,
Boys and girls, their lives polluted,
History will always bear the scars
Of man's mistakes.

Chorus

3. Press the button, pull the lever,
Are we sure, check the computer –
Man's inventions hold us in their power.
If we do not stem the tide
Of man's irrational behaviour,
There'll be no one left alive to hear
Of man's mistake.

Index

Acknowledgements

The publishers gratefully acknowledge permission to reproduce the following copyright material:

© 1992 Clive Barnwell for 'All sorts of people', 'Don't let the sunny days go', 'Robin Hood', 'See the river run', 'The land that time forgot', 'The whale' and 'We'll all reach out'; © 1992 Ian Henderson Begg for 'Going round the fair', 'Hay time', 'It's our job (The media song)', 'Pollution is banned' and 'Round the seasons'; © 1992 Ann Bryant for 'Chop, chop', 'Colours', 'Fire', 'Life in the sun', 'Mum! mum! Quickly come', 'My tune has a magic murmur', 'Once upon a summer's day', 'Owl can't go to sleep', 'Technology grind', 'The winter castle', 'Thread of my dreams', 'Toc toc toc', and 'What Annie McRae wanted for tea'; © Debbie Campbell for 'Caterpillar lullaby' (1989), 'Christmas at school' (music only, 1988), 'Getting around' (1992), 'Lonely panda waltz' (1988), 'Traffic song' (1992), 'Travelling man' (1988) and 'Wake up, wake up, wake up' (1988); © 1992 Elizabeth Chapman (words only) for 'Be my valentine', 'Pancake song' and 'Real tennis rag'; ©1990 Veronica Clark for 'Goodness how you've grown'; © 1992 Elena Davies (music only) for 'Circle of love'; © Leonora Davies for 'Circle of love' (1992), 'Take a pocketful of prayers (1980), 'The big beasts' boogie' (1980), 'The magic tree' (1992) and 'You're smiling' (1983); © 1988 Jaqui Dillon for 'Christmas at school' (words only); © Mike Fenton for 'Apples and bananas' (arrangement only), 'Bounce kangaroo bounce' and 'International Brother John' (arrangement only); © Lesley Funge for 'Entering Jerusalem' (1991) and 'Tell it to the world' (1990); © 1992 Gerald Haigh for 'A man coming through', 'Leonardo' and 'Our Christmas prayer'; © Sandra Kerr for 'Light up Diwali'; © 1989 Jane Morgan for 'What are you wearing?'; © Peter Morrell for 'Age of the chip' (1992), 'A year full of songs' (1992), 'Ballad of Moses' (1992), 'Be my valentine' (music only, 1992), 'Earth, air, fire and water' (1992), 'Flying high' (1992), 'F.R.I.E.N.D.S' (1992), 'Harvest' (1988), 'Looking back, looking forward' (1992), 'One world family' (1992), 'Pancake song' (music only, 1992), 'People for peace' (1986), 'Real tennis rag' (music only, 1992), 'Saints live on!' (1992), 'Send our love around the world' (1992), 'The chug-chug song' (1992), 'The conker song' (1992), 'There go our festivals' (1992), 'The Weather-or-Nots' (1992), 'The world we live in' (1992), 'Walter Raleigh blues' (1992), and 'Way up high' (1992); © David Moses for 'A king riding on a donkey' (1992), 'At the ripe old age of one' (1986), 'Black hole' (1992), 'Brixton market' (1992), 'Chicks grow into chickens' (1992), 'Doctor, Doctor' (1978), 'Eeny meeny minibeasts' (1992), 'Eighteen spiders' (1984), 'Giving and getting' (1976), 'Going back to school' (1992), 'Hanukka candles' (1989), 'I know they're bad for my teeth' (1987), 'I'm so hot' (1987), 'It's a monster, isn't it?' (1984), 'Life in the rainforest' (1992), 'Me and my world' (1992), 'Motor car' (1970), 'Mrs Govinder Singh' (1992), 'My friend Billy loves bubble gum' (1976), 'Our school cook' (1984), 'Poles apart' (1992), 'Rain drops' (1992), 'Ring bells, ring' (1984), 'Rocket to the stars, rocket to the moon' (1984), 'Scratch my tummy like a chimpanzee' (1992), 'Shine cold, shine hot' (1992), 'Snow all over the ground' (1992), 'The camel has got the hump' (1987) and 'The orangutang song' (1985); © 1992 Gillian Parker for 'Brrr!', 'Christmas eve', 'Famous names', 'Foot work', How did we travel?', 'How the world began', 'Into orbit', 'It's noisy', 'Lots of weather!', 'My pets', 'Say 'Thanks'', 'See the world', 'Send a message', 'Sounds', 'Sunshine', 'Travel by water' and 'Winter rock'; © 1992 Howard Skempton for 'It's never the time or place'; © Chris Williams for 'Desert round' (1987), 'I am the water' (1992), 'Summer on the river' (1992), 'The herb song' (1992) and 'The song of the winter wind' (1992).

Every effort has been made to trace copyright holders for the songs in this anthology and the publishers apologise for any inadvertant omissions.